Anti-Inflammatory Cookbook

Delicious Recipes to Reduce Inflammation and Improve Health

Marta Baker

Table of Contents

WHAT IS
AN ANTI-INFLAMMATORY DIET?

Foods classified as anti-inflammatory have been shown to lessen inflammation in the body. Although inflammation is a normal reaction to damage or infection, it can also be a chronic condition that worsens a number of illnesses, such as diabetes, heart disease, and arthritis.

Some examples of anti-inflammatory foods include:

Fruits and vegetables: These are high in antioxidants, which can help reduce inflammation. Examples include berries, cherries, citrus fruits, leafy greens, and cruciferous vegetables like broccoli and cauliflower.

Whole grains: Whole grains like brown rice, quinoa, and whole wheat are high in fiber, which can help reduce inflammation.

Fatty fish: Fatty fish like salmon, tuna, and sardines are high in omega-3 fatty acids, which have anti-inflammatory properties.

Nuts and seeds: Nuts and seeds like almonds, walnuts, and flaxseeds are high in healthy fats and fiber, which can help reduce inflammation.

Spices: Certain spices like turmeric, ginger, and cinnamon have been shown to have anti-inflammatory properties.

It's important to note that while incorporating anti-inflammatory foods into your diet can be beneficial, it's also important to maintain a balanced diet that includes a variety of nutrient-rich foods.

ANTI-INFLAMMATORY DIET BASICS

A diet that aims to reduce inflammation in the body is referred to as an anti-inflammatory diet. Chronic inflammation has been linked to numerous health issues, including diabetes, heart disease, and certain cancers.

The fundamental principles of an anti-inflammatory diet are as follows:

Consume plenty of fruits and vegetables: Fruits and vegetables are abundant in antioxidants and other essential nutrients that can help decrease inflammation. Aim to eat a variety of colorful fruits and vegetables every day.

Choose healthy fats: Healthy fats found in foods like nuts, seeds, fatty fish, and olive oil can help decrease inflammation. Avoid saturated and trans fats found in processed foods, fried foods, and baked goods.

Incorporate whole grains: Whole grains, such as brown rice, quinoa, and whole-wheat bread, are packed with fiber and can help decrease inflammation.

Reduce your intake of processed foods: Processed foods are often high in sugar, unhealthy fats, and refined carbohydrates, all of which can contribute to inflammation. Try to limit your consumption of processed foods and choose whole, nutrient-dense foods instead.

Limit your consumption of animal products: Animal products like meat and dairy can be high in saturated fat, which can contribute to inflammation. Try to limit your intake of animal products and opt for plant-based sources of protein, such as beans and lentils.

Use herbs and spices: Many herbs and spices, such as turmeric, ginger, and garlic, possess anti-inflammatory properties and can be used to add flavor to your meals.

Remember, an anti-inflammatory diet is just one aspect of a healthy lifestyle. It is crucial to engage in regular exercise, manage stress, and get enough sleep to reduce inflammation and promote overall health.

BREAKFAST RECIPES

GRAPEFRUIT, GINGER, AND TURMERIC LASSI

Servings: 1

INGREDIENTS:

- 250 ml of natural yogurt
- Juice of 1/2 large grapefruit
- 1 piece of fresh ginger
- 1/2 teaspoon of ground turmeric
- A pinch of salt
- 1-2 tablespoons of honey or agave syrup
- Water as needed

INSTRUCTIONS:

1. Wash the grapefruit, cut it in half, and squeeze the juice. We should get about half a glass of liquid. We can strain it to remove the pulp or leave it as it is, ensuring no seeds have been strained.

2. Cut a small piece of ginger, depending on your tolerance for this product, peel and chop very finely, or grate using a suitable grater. Put the yogurt with its whey, juice, ginger, turmeric, a small pinch of salt, and a tablespoon of honey in a blender or grinder.

3. Blend everything well, mixing until you get a homogeneous texture without lumps. Taste and adjust the sweetness level to our liking by adding more honey. If it is too thick, add a little water or more juice. Serve immediately.

NUTRITIONAL VALUES:

- Calories: 216 kcal
- Fat: 2.9 g
- Carbohydrates: 39.7 g
- Fiber: 0.4 g
- Protein: 10.8 g

SUGAR-FREE OATMEAL COOKIES

Servings: 10

INGREDIENTS:

- Eggs: 2
- Mashed pumpkin: 150g
- Ground cinnamon: 2.5ml
- Vanilla: 2.5ml
- Oatmeal: 170g
- Chia seeds: 1 teaspoon
- Flax seeds: 1 teaspoon
- Raw almonds, chopped, in sticks or slices: 50g
- Raisins: 50g

INSTRUCTIONS:

1. First, preheat the oven to 180°C and prepare one or two trays by covering them with parchment paper or some non-stick material suitable for the oven.

2. Place the eggs with the pumpkin, cinnamon, and vanilla in a medium bowl, and beat with a hand whisk until everything is well integrated. Add the salt, rolled oats, chia and flax seeds, and almonds. Mix with a spatula or blade and add the raisins or larger chopped dried fruit at the end.

3. Combine well to have a homogeneous dough and form cookies taking small portions with a few teaspoons. They form better if we take the dough with one and use the other, moistened, to deposit the portion. With wet fingers, we can finally give them a more rounded shape.

4. We could also leave the dough to rest in the fridge for a few hours to cool down and thus form them with our

hands more easily. Nothing will grow in the oven, so we can make them thicker if we want them to be tender on the inside or thinner if we want them to be more crunchy.

5. Sprinkle with a little cinnamon if desired, and bake for 15-18 minutes or until golden to taste. Wait a bit and let cool completely on a wire rack.

NUTRITIONAL VALUES:

- Calories: 103
- fat: 5.2g
- carbohydrate: 11.8g
- fiber: 2.3g
- Protein: 3.7g

TROPICAL SMOOTHIE WITH TURMERIC.

Servings: 1

INGREDIENTS:

- 1 cup frozen mango
- 1/2 cup fresh pineapple
- 1/3 cup coconut water
- 2 tablespoons plain Greek yogurt (unsweetened)
- 1/4 teaspoon ground cinnamon
- 1/4 teaspoon ground turmeric

INSTRUCTIONS:

1. Cut the pineapple into small cubes.
2. Place all the ingredients in a high-powered blender. Blend until all the ingredients are fully integrated and have a smooth consistency.

NUTRITIONAL VALUES:

- Calories: 190
- Fat: 2g
- Carbohydrates: 40g
- Fiber: 5g
- Protein: 8g

GOLDEN MILK

Servings: 2

INGREDIENTS:

- Vegetable milk or drink: 500ml
- Cinnamon stick: 1
- Cloves: 2
- Green cardamom: 1
- Fresh ginger: 5g
- Black peppercorns: 2
- Ground turmeric: 5g
- Honey: 15ml
- Ground cinnamon, to taste

INSTRUCTIONS:

1. Heat the milk in a pan with the cinnamon stick, the cloves, the open cardamom, the peppercorns, and the chopped or ground ginger. Lower the heat before it reaches a boil, and add the turmeric, stirring well. Cook over very low heat for at least 5 minutes.

2. Strain and add honey or a vegetable alternative to taste. Divide into cups and serve with a little ground cinnamon on top. It can also be whipped with a cappuccino blender to make it fluffy or served with a cloud of milk.

NUTRITIONAL VALUES:

- Calories: 120
- Fat: 4g
- Carbohydrate: 19g
- Fiber: 2g
- Protein: 3g

CHERRY COCONUT PORRIDGE

Servings: 2

INGREDIENTS:

- 1.5 cups oats
- 4 tablespoons chia seeds
- 3-4 cups of coconut drinking milk
- 3 tablespoons raw cacao
- Pinch of stevia
- Coconut shavings
- Cherries (fresh or frozen)
- Dark chocolate shavings
- Maple syrup

INSTRUCTIONS:

1. Combine oats, chia, coconut milk, cacao, and stevia in a saucepan. Bring to a boil over medium flame and then simmer over lower heat until the oats are cooked.

2. Pour into a bowl and top with coconut shavings, cherries, dark chocolate shavings, and maple syrup to taste.

NUTRITIONAL VALUES:

- Calories: 459
- Fat: 20.3g
- Carbohydrate: 60.8g
- Fiber: 18.4g
- Protein: 13.2g

GINGERBREAD OATMEAL

Servings: 2

INGREDIENTS:

- 4 cups water
- 2 cups old-fashioned oats
- 1 1/2 tbsp. ground cinnamon
- 1/4 tsp. ground coriander
- 1/4 tsp. ground cloves
- 1/4 tsp. ground ginger
- 1/4 tsp. ground allspice
- 1/4 tsp. ground cardamom
- 1/8 tsp. ground nutmeg
- Sweetener

INSTRUCTIONS:

1. Add the water to a pot and boil it.
2. Add the oats.
3. Add the spices.
4. Stir occasionally until the oats are done. Stir in your sweetener to taste and serve.

NUTRITIONAL VALUES:

- Calories: 193 kcal
- Protein: 6 g
- Fat: 3 g
- Carbohydrates: 34 g
- Fiber: 5 g

RASPBERRY MUESLI

Servings: 2

INGREDIENTS:

- 250g frozen raspberries (unsweetened!)
- 250g low-fat quark
- Approx. 150-200ml of low-fat milk
- 6 tbsp fine whole meal oat flakes
- 20g walnuts

INSTRUCTIONS:

1. Thaw the raspberries. It is best to take the raspberries out of the freezer one night before and let them thaw in the fridge overnight

2. Mix the low-fat quark with the milk until smooth and stir in the whole-meal rolled oats.

3. Mix the quark with the raspberries and sprinkle with the walnuts.

NUTRITIONAL VALUES:

- Calories: 236 kcal
- Protein: 14 g
- Fat: 9 g
- Carbohydrates: 26 g
- Fiber: 8 g

WHOLE GRAIN BREAD WITH AVOCADO, EGG CREAM CHEESE

Servings: 1

INGREDIENTS:

- 2 slices of whole meal bread
- 1 hard-boiled egg
- 1/4 avocado
- 100g low-fat cream cheese (alternatively cottage cheese)
- Herb salt
- Pepper

INSTRUCTIONS:

1. Peel and finely chop the egg. Take the avocado and chop it finely.
2. Mix the egg and avocado with the cream cheese and season with herb salt and pepper.
3. Spread the avocado egg cream cheese on the two slices of whole meal bread and enjoy.

NUTRITIONAL VALUES:

- Calories: 475
- Protein: 23g
- Fat: 24g
- Carbohydrates: 44g
- Fiber: 14g

ANTI-INFLAMMATORY YOGURT

Servings: 1

INGREDIENTS:

- 4 tablespoons natural yogurt
- 1 pinch of cinnamon
- 1 pinch of turmeric powder
- 1 pinch of ginger powder
- 1 pinch of chili powder
- 2 tbsp linseed oil
- Chopped nuts or almonds, if you like
- Fruit as desired, e.g., 1/2 papaya

INSTRUCTIONS:

1. Mix the yogurt with the anti-inflammatory spices and the linseed oil.
2. Add 1 handful of chopped nuts/almonds and 1 handful of fruit according to taste and individual tolerance.

NUTRITIONAL VALUES:

- Calories: 314 kcal
- Protein: 8.9 g
- Fat: 29.6 g
- Carbohydrates: 7.2 g
- Fiber: 2.8 g

TURMERIC-ORANGE PORRIDGE

Servings: 2

INGREDIENTS:

- 1 organic orange, zest and juice
- 1 pinch of turmeric powder
- 60g oatmeal
- 1 tsp ground flaxseed
- 200ml soy milk
- 100g low-fat quark/yogurt or a soy alternative
- Fruit and toppings of your choice

INSTRUCTIONS:

1. Wash off the organic orange with hot water. Finely grate about a teaspoon of the peel. Halve the orange with a knife and press through an orange press. We need the juice of half an orange.

2. Place oatmeal, flaxseed, turmeric, and orange zest in a microwave-safe bowl. (Alternatively, you can also cook the porridge in a pot on the stove). Pour in the milk, stir, and microwave for 1:30 minutes. Stir once and heat for another 30 seconds. Then let it steep for about 1 minute.

3. Stir in low-fat quark and orange juice and top with your favorite fruit, nut butter, or crunchy muesli.

NUTRITIONAL VALUES:

- Calories: 281 kcal
- Protein: 15 g
- Carbohydrates: 39 g
- Fiber: 7 g Fat: 7 g

PORRIDGE WITH BLUEBERRIES AND ALMONDS

Servings: 1

INGREDIENTS:

- 200 ml oat milk
- 50 g rolled oats (gluten-free)
- 1 tsp agave syrup
- 2 tbsp almonds (unpeeled)
- 50 g blueberries

INSTRUCTIONS:

1. Heat almond milk in a saucepan. Stir in the oats and agave syrup and simmer briefly over medium heat. Then let it simmer for about 5 minutes over low heat.

2. Wash the blueberries and pat dry. Roughly chop the almonds. Give both over the broth.

NUTRITIONAL VALUES:

- Calories: 482 kcal
- Protein 16 g
- Fat 23 g
- Carbohydrates 52 g

CHIA SEED PUDDING WITH MANGO

Servings: 1

INGREDIENTS:

- 250ml almond milk
- 30g chia seeds
- 1/2 mango
- Juice of 1/2 orange

INSTRUCTIONS:

1. Stir the chia seeds into the almond milk with a whisk and leave to soak in the fridge for at least 30 minutes, if possible overnight.

2. Peel and core the mango and cut it into small pieces. Squeeze the orange, mix the mango pieces with a little juice, and leave to infuse briefly.

3. Serve the chia pudding garnished with mango pieces.

NUTRITIONAL VALUES:

- Calories: 275 kcal
- Protein 9 g
- Fat 13 g
- Carbohydrates 25 g

OATMEAL AND ROSEHIP POWDER

Servings: 2

INGREDIENTS:

- Oatmeal: 60g
- Oat bran: 1 teaspoon / 3g
- Natural oat milk: 250ml
- Apple: 1 piece / 250g
- Cinnamon: 1 teaspoon / 1g
- Maple syrup: 1 teaspoon / 8g
- Rosehip powder: 1 tablespoon / 10g
- Sunflower seeds: 1 tablespoon / 15g
- Hemp oil: 2 teaspoons / 12g

INSTRUCTIONS:

1. Boil the oat milk in a small saucepan. Once the oat milk is boiling, reduce the flame and stir in the rolled oats and oat bran. Simmer on low heat for about 3 minutes, stirring now and then. Turn off the stove.

2. Tip: Use a lid; it's faster and saves electricity. Or soak oatmeal and bran in the fridge overnight.

3. While the porridge is cooling: wash, core, and dice the apple. Add apple pieces, cinnamon, and maple syrup, and mix.

4. Finally, stir in rosehip powder (especially helpful against joint pain) and hemp oil and divide the anti-inflammatory porridge into two bowls.

5. Sprinkle with sunflower seeds and enjoy with other fruit, nuts, or seeds if desired. The perfect anti-inflammatory breakfast against rheumatism and all other inflammations is ready.

NUTRITIONAL VALUES:

- Calories: 481
- Protein2.55g
- Carbohydrates17.11g
- Fat 3.91g

QUARK WITH WALNUT AND CARROT

Servings: 1

INGREDIENTS:

- Low-fat quark (organic): 125g
- Tigernut Flour: 1 tablespoon / 10g
- Flaxseed (crushed): 2 tablespoons / 16g
- Oat bran flakes: 1 tablespoon / 5g
- Almond butter: 1 tablespoon / 15g
- Natural oat milk: 50ml
- Chia seeds: 2 teaspoons / 10g
- Walnuts: 8 pieces / 10g
- Linseed oil (native, organic): 1 teaspoon / 6g
- Carrots: 1 piece / 50g

INSTRUCTIONS:

1. Peel and finely grate a small carrot. Slightly chop the walnuts.
2. Mix well the oat bran, almond butter, chia seeds, linseed oil, quark, linseed, and tiger nut flour. Stir in the walnuts, and grated carrots, and the slightly sweet, healthy quark breakfast is ready.
3. A cucumber instead of a carrot also tastes good in this healthy quark breakfast.

NUTRITIONAL VALUES:

- Calories548
- protein 9.52g
- carbohydrates8.45g
- Fat11.74g

TIGERNUT WAFFLES

Servings: 2

INGREDIENTS:

- Tigernut Flour: 75g
- Oatmeal (gluten-free): 125g
- Natural oat milk: 150ml
- Cinnamon: 1 pinch / 1g
- Water: 70g
- Coconut oil: 3 tablespoons / 25g

INSTRUCTIONS:

1. Finely grind the oat flakes with a smoothie maker or in a grain mill. Add the tiger nut flour, oat milk, 2 tbsp coconut oil, water, and cinnamon, and mix well. Let the dough swell for 10 minutes, then add some water if necessary. The batter should be quite runny so that the waffle batter spreads well and the waffles stay light and fluffy.

2. Preheat the waffle iron and brush both sides thinly with coconut oil using a brush. Place the oatmeal and Tigernut waffle batter in the center of the waffle iron and spread evenly. Close the waffle iron and bake each waffle for about 3 minutes until golden.

3. Homemade apple sauce or berry sauce goes well with this. The waffle batter is enough for about 4 waffles, i.e., 2 healthy waffles per person.

NUTRITIONAL VALUES:

- Calories 554
- Protein 4.73g
- Carbohydrates 29.56g
- Fat 12.13g

FRUIT SALAD WITH NUTS

Servings: 2

INGREDIENTS:

- Organic apple: 1 piece / 150g
- Strawberries: 100g
- Orange: 150g
- Hazelnuts: 10pcs /20g
- Flaxseed (crushed): 1 tablespoon / 15g
- Walnuts: 4 pieces / 25g
- Linseed oil (native): 1 teaspoon / 5g
- Omega 3 algae oil: 1 teaspoon / 5g

INSTRUCTIONS:

1. Wash the fruit, remove the core or peel, and cut it into bite-sized pieces. Chop the nuts.
2. Stir linseed oil, algae oil, flaxseed, and chopped nuts into the fruit salad. Mix well. You can vary the types of fruit as you wish.

NUTRITIONAL VALUES:

- Calories: 327
- Protein: 2.87g
- Carbohydrates: 9.21g
- Fat: 9.92g

SMOOTHIE BOWL

Servings: 2

INGREDIENTS:

- Banana: 1 piece / 115g
- Blueberries (frozen): 200g
- Coconut yogurt: 3 tablespoons / 45g
- Almond milk (no additives): 100 milliliters
- Oatmeal: 2 tablespoons / 12g
- Goji berries: 2 teaspoons / 10g
- Chia seeds: 2 teaspoons / 6g
- Pumpkin seeds: 2 teaspoons / 10g
- Sunflower seeds: 2 teaspoons / 10g
- Soft fruit: 2 tablespoons / 20g

INSTRUCTIONS:

1. Peel and coarsely chop the banana. Pour into an oblong container (about a measuring cup).
2. Add the frozen blueberries, coconut yogurt, oat flakes, and almond milk, and puree everything with a hand blender to a creamy mass. Add more liquid if necessary.
3. Divide the smoothie mixture between 2 bowls and sprinkle each bowl with 1 teaspoon of chia seeds, sunflower seeds, pumpkin seeds, goji berries, and other berries. Your vitamin breakfast is ready!

NUTRITIONAL VALUES:

- Calories: 228
- Protein: 2.69g
- Carbohydrates: 10.87g
- Fat: 3.07g

OATMEAL WITH NUTS

Servings: 1

INGREDIENTS:

- 150 milliliters of natural oat milk
- 6 pieces / 15 g of walnuts
- 2 tablespoons / 12g of chia seeds
- 1 tablespoon / 15g of organic wheat germ
- 1 tablespoon / 25g of almond butter
- 2 tablespoons / 25g of organic coconut flour
- 75 grams of wild blueberries
- 1 teaspoon / 5g of native organic linseed oil
- 2 g of cinnamon
- 1 tablespoon (heaped) / 10 g of tigernut flour

INSTRUCTIONS:

1. Chop walnuts and defrost wild blueberries in advance.
2. In a bowl, mix oat milk, organic linseed oil, wheat germ, coconut flour, walnuts, chia seeds, almond butter, and cinnamon.
3. Stir in the blueberries and walnuts and sprinkle a few on top for garnish.
4. You can also add other fruits such as apples or bananas.

NUTRITIONAL VALUES:

- Calories: 666
- Protein: 19.89g
- Carbohydrates: 37.33g
- Fat: 43.37g

FLEA SEED YOGURT WITH BERRIES

Servings: 2

INGREDIENTS:

- 300 grams of coconut yogurt
- 1 tablespoon / 3g of ground flea seed shells
- 1 teaspoon / 3g of chia seeds
- 1 teaspoon / 5g of shelled hemp seeds
- 100 grams of strawberries
- 100 grams of blueberries
- 1 tablespoon / 5g of coconut flakes

INSTRUCTIONS:

1. Mix coconut yogurt with chia seeds, ground flea seed shells, and shelled hemp seeds, and let it sit for a while to thicken.

2. Clean the strawberries and wash the blueberries. Cut the strawberries in half.

3. Divide the yogurt and seed mixture between two bowls, add coconut flakes, and garnish with fresh fruit. You can also add cocoa nibs or nuts.

NUTRITIONAL VALUES:

- Calories: 356
- Protein: 4.77g
- Carbohydrates: 14.25g
- Fat: 15.45g

OMEGA 3 SMOOTHIE WITH ALGAE OIL

Servings: 2

INGREDIENTS:

- 2 pieces / 200g of kiwi
- 1 piece / 120g of banana
- 80 grams of frozen spinach
- 2 pieces / 120g of carrots
- 2 tablespoons / 12g of lemon juice
- 1 tablespoon / 15g of raw cacao bean
- 2 teaspoons / 6g of omega 3 algae oil
- 200 milliliters of water

INSTRUCTIONS:

1. Wash and cut the carrots into pieces. Peel the kiwis and banana.

2. Add everything in the blender or smoothie maker with lemon juice, water, and raw cacao beans. Defrost the spinach properly or use small portions of frozen spinach.

3. Blend everything into a creamy smoothie for about 1 minute at full speed. Add 2 teaspoons of omega-3 algae oil just before the end. Serve immediately.

4. The quantity is sufficient with the specified amount of water for 2 large glasses of 300 ml each and is quite dense. The smoothie should therefore be served with a spoon. You can adjust the consistency by adding more water. For sweeter taste, use two bananas.

NUTRITIONAL VALUES:

- Calories: 191
- Protein: 4.90g
- Carbohydrates: 26.50g
- Fat: 5.84g

COTTAGE CHEESE AND OAT

Servings: 2

INGREDIENTS:

- 200 grams of organic cottage cheese
- 5 tablespoons (heaped) / 50 g of oatmeal
- 150 grams of natural yogurt
- 2 tablespoons / 15g of crushed flaxseed
- 2 tablespoons / 15g of pumpkin seeds
- 1 teaspoon / 7g of honey
- 10 g of ginger
- 1/2 teaspoon / 1g of cinnamon
- 80 grams of blackberries
- 1 pinch / 1 g of salt

INSTRUCTIONS:

1. Peel and finely grate the ginger or use ginger powder.
2. Whisk together the cottage cheese, yogurt, cinnamon, honey, flaxseeds, rolled oats, salt, and ginger in a bowl.
3. Wash blackberries and add them on top. You can use other berries if you prefer.
4. Divide the cottage cheese oatmeal between two bowls and sprinkle with the pumpkin seeds and blackberries.

NUTRITIONAL VALUES:

- Calories: 349
- Protein: 23.44g
- Carbohydrates: 28.11g
- Fat: 15.49g

ZUCCHINI AND FETA MUFFINS

Servings: 3

INGREDIENTS:

- 3 pieces / 700g of zucchini
- 3 pieces / 165g of organic eggs
- 40 grams of almond flour
- 40 grams of lupine flour
- 2 teaspoons / 10g of salt
- 1 teaspoon / 1g of black pepper
- 3 branches / 30g of fresh parsley
- 2 branches / 20g of fresh basil
- 200 grams of feta cheese

INSTRUCTIONS:

1. Wash and grate zucchini with peel. Sprinkle salt over the grated zucchini and leave it to stand for 30 minutes. Then squeeze the zucchini into a sieve.

2. Chop the feta and finely chop the herbs. Preheat the oven to 175 degrees.

3. Place zucchini in a bowl. Mix with eggs, almond and lupine flour, pepper, herbs, and feta. Season with the remaining salt, depending on how salty the feta is.

4. Line 12 muffin tins with paper cups. Divide the batter into molds and bake for around 25 minutes.

NUTRITIONAL VALUES:

- Calories: 337
- Protein: 23.28g
- Carbohydrates: 7.46g
- Fat: 22.86g

LUPINE PATTIES WITH RAW CARROTS

Servings: 2

INGREDIENTS:

- 400 grams of lupins (jar)
- 2 pieces / 110g of organic eggs
- 5 tablespoons / 32g of gluten-free oatmeal
- 2 pieces / 50g of spring onions
- 1 piece / 3g of garlic cloves
- 6 tablespoons / 60g of virgin olive oil
- 2 teaspoons / 10g of salt
- 1 gram of freshly ground white pepper
- 5 pieces / 400g of carrots
- 1 tablespoon / 14g of vinegar
- 30 grams of pumpkin seeds

INSTRUCTIONS:

1. Drain the lupine seeds and chop them in a blender. Mix with eggs, rolled oats, 1 teaspoon salt, pepper, 1 tablespoon olive oil, chopped spring onions, and crushed garlic cloves to form a firm dough. Leave to soak for 10 minutes.

2. Peel and grate carrots. Mix with vinegar, 1 tablespoon of olive oil, salt, pepper, and pumpkin seeds, and season to taste.

3. Form eight patties from the lupine dough and fry in the olive oil until golden brown on both sides.

4. Serve immediately with raw carrots. The patties also taste good when cold.

NUTRITIONAL VALUES:

- Calories: 544
- Protein: 30.55g
- Carbohydrates: 21.17g
- Fat: 35.73g

ZUCCHINI FETA MUFFINS

Servings: 3

INGREDIENTS:

- 3 pieces / 700g of zucchini
- 3 pieces / 165g of organic eggs
- 40 grams of almond flour
- 40 grams of lupine flour
- 2 teaspoons / 10g of salt
- 1 teaspoon / 1g of black pepper
- 3 branches / 30g of fresh parsley
- 2 branches / 20g of fresh basil
- 200 grams of feta cheese

INSTRUCTIONS:

1. Wash and grate zucchini with peel. Sprinkle salt over the grated zucchini and leave it to stand for 30 minutes. Then squeeze the zucchini into a sieve.
2. Chop the feta and finely chop the herbs. Preheat the oven to 175 degrees.
3. Place zucchini in a bowl. Mix with eggs, almond and lupine flour, pepper, herbs, and feta. Season with the remaining salt, depending on how salty the feta is.
4. Line 12 muffin tins with paper cups. Divide the batter into molds and bake for around 25 minutes.

NUTRITIONAL VALUES:

- Calories: 337
- Protein: 23.28g
- Carbohydrates: 7.46g
- Fat: 22.86g

QUINOA COCONUT YOGURT

Servings: 1

INGREDIENTS:

- 150 grams of coconut yogurt (8% fat)
- 30 grams of quinoa
- 1 tablespoon / 15g of walnuts
- 1 tablespoon / 12g of crushed flaxseed
- 1 pinch / 1g of cinnamon
- 2 teaspoons / 8g of grated coconut
- 75 grams of blueberries
- 1 pinch / 1g of salt
- 1/2 teaspoon / 5g of honey

INSTRUCTIONS:

1. Wash the quinoa in a sieve and prepare according to the package instructions with a pinch of salt.
2. Chop the walnuts large. Wash and dry blueberries. Put a few berries aside for decoration.
3. Mix the quinoa, cinnamon, blueberries, walnuts, flaxseed, shredded coconut, honey, and coconut yogurt (as a vegan alternative).

NUTRITIONAL VALUES:

- Calories: 510
- Protein: 12.57g
- Carbohydrates: 37.76g
- Fat: 34.20g

OAT AND HEMP SEED PORRIDGE

Servings: 2

INGREDIENTS:

- 80 grams of oatmeal
- 2 tablespoons / 20g of oat bran
- 5 tablespoons / 40g of hemp seeds
- 1 piece / 125g of apple
- 3 tablespoons / 25g of crushed flaxseed
- 500 milliliters of natural oat drink
- 1 pinch / 1g of salt
- 1 pinch / 1g of ground vanilla

INSTRUCTIONS:

1. Mix the oatmeal, bran, and flaxseed with the oat milk in a saucepan. Add a pinch of salt and vanilla. Bring to a boil over medium heat. Stir occasionally in between. Simmer for 5 minutes, stirring constantly.

2. Let the porridge cool down a bit (about 7 minutes). Stir in the hemp seeds and serve.

3. Wash, core, and cut the apple into pieces. Scatter the apple pieces over the porridge and serve.

NUTRITIONAL VALUES:

- Calories 500
- Protein 17.76g
- Carbohydrates 57.44g
- Fat 20.69g

SMOOTHIE WITH AVOCADO & MINT

Servings: 2

Ingredients:

- 60 grams frozen spinach
- 20 fresh peppermint leaves (15g)
- 1 piece of ginger (8g)
- 2 tablespoons of lemon juice (16g)
- 300 grams of coconut water
- 1 ripe avocado (160g)
- 1 slightly ripe banana (100g)

Instructions:

1. Defrost frozen spinach (removable in portions) or use a suitable blender in good time. Alternatively, wash three hands of baby spinach or spinach leaves (approx. 60g) and the peppermint leaves and place them in the smoothie maker or a tall container.

2. Grate the ginger and add to the blender with the avocado, banana, coconut water, and lemon juice. Blend everything into a creamy green smoothie.

Nutritional Values:

- Calories: 178
- Protein: 3.32g
- Carbohydrates: 16.14g
- Fat: 10.92g

OMEGA 3 BREAD

Servings: 8

Ingredients:

- 350 grams of wholemeal spelled flour
- 50 grams of soy flour
- 100 grams of spelled flour
- 50 grams of flaxseed flour (gluten-free)
- 80 grams of walnuts
- 75 grams of crushed flaxseed
- 20 grams of pumpkin seeds
- 80 grams of shelled hemp seeds
- 3 tablespoons of chia seeds (20g)
- 1 pack of dry baker's yeast (17g)
- 3 tablespoons of walnut oil (16g)
- 1 1/2 teaspoons of sugar (6g)
- 1 1/2 teaspoons of salt (6g)
- 1 teaspoon of bread spice (3g)
- 300 milliliters of water

Instructions:

1. Coarsely chop the walnuts.
2. Mix all dry ingredients (soy flour, flaxseed flour, spelled flour, wholemeal spelled flour, dry baking yeast, salt, bread spices, sugar, ground flaxseeds, walnuts, hemp seeds, pumpkin seeds, chia seeds). Add oil and warm water and knead by hand for at least 10 minutes. It's faster with a kneading machine or a Thermomix.

3. Let the dough rise warmly under a cloth for 30 minutes, then knead again for 5 minutes. Form the dough into a loaf and let it stand again under a cloth in a warm place for 45 minutes until it increases twice in size.

4. Preheat oven to 175 degrees. Sprinkle the bread with seeds, score in a diamond shape, and bake on a baking sheet for approx. 40 minutes.

5. About 25 slices can be cut from the omega-3 bread. By the way, it cuts easier after cooling. A portion is calculated with 3 slices of omega-3 bread.

6. This bread is particularly rich in omega-3. It contains 3 grams of plant-based omega-3 per disc. This is how you promote heart health. Because of the nuts and seeds, it has fewer carbohydrates than regular bread.

Nutritional Values:

- Calories: 470
- Protein: 20.29g
- Carbohydrates: 41.34g
- Fat: 24.44g

OAT RASPBERRY SHAKE

Servings: 2

INGREDIENTS:

- 200g frozen raspberries
- 2 tablespoons (20g) almond butter
- 3 tablespoons (40g) oatmeal
- 300 milliliters water
- 2 teaspoons (10g) glucose (optional)

INSTRUCTIONS:

1. Let the raspberries thaw or wash them in a high-performance blender with the other ingredients or mix them well in a high mixing bowl with a hand blender.

NUTRITIONAL VALUES:

- Calories 193
- Protein 5.51g
- carbohydrates 23.90g
- Fat 7.55g

HIGH PROTEIN SKYR QUINOA

Servings: 2

INGREDIENTS:

- 400g skyr
- 80g quinoa
- 3 tablespoons (40g) chopped almonds
- 2 tablespoons (25g) shelled hemp seeds
- 1 pinch (1g) salt
- 1 banana (120g)
- 1 pinch (1g) ground vanilla

INSTRUCTIONS:

1. Prepare quinoa according to package instructions and allow to cool.
2. Cut the banana into pieces.
3. Mix the quinoa, vanilla, banana, hemp seeds, almonds, and skyr.

NUTRITIONAL VALUES:

- Calories 501
- protein 35.91g
- carbohydrates 45.98g
- Fat 22.85g

MANGO AND BANANA SMOOTHIE BOWL

Servings: 1

INGREDIENTS:

- 1 small, very ripe mango
- 1 ripe banana (half frozen and half natural)
- 2-4 tablespoons plain yogurt
- 1 pinch of ground turmeric
- Lime or lemon juice
- 2 teaspoons chia seeds
- 1 tablespoon pumpkin seeds
- 1 teaspoon peeled and chopped almonds
- 2 tablespoons fresh or frozen berries

INSTRUCTIONS:

1. Peel the mango and chop it, collecting the juices that it releases. Blend in a blender, food processor, or food processor. Add the yogurt and blend a little more. Add half of the frozen banana and blend with the turmeric until it is incorporated into the base cream. Taste and add lime or lemon juice or more yogurt as we like.

2. Mix well and arrange in a bowl that is not very flat. Complete by adding the rest of the peeled and sliced banana, the chia seeds, the pumpkin seeds, and the red fruits, which can be straight from the freezer. Finish with some almonds, which we can lightly toast in a pan without oil.

NUTRITIONAL VALUES:

- Calories: 356
- Fat: 13g
- Carbohydrates: 58g
- Fiber: 12g
- Protein: 10g

COCONUT AND HEMP BARS

Servings: 8

INGREDIENTS:

- 1 cup organic hemp hearts
- 1 cup shredded organic coconut, unsweetened
- 1 cup almond butter
- 1/3 cup organic maple syrup
- 1 teaspoon ground cinnamon

INSTRUCTIONS:

1. Preheat the oven to 160 degrees Celsius.

2. Spread the coconut on a baking sheet for 5-10 minutes or until completely golden. At the same time, mix the hemp hearts, almond butter, maple syrup, and ground cinnamon in a bowl.

3. Add the toasted coconut and mix well. Press the mixture into a previously buttered baking pan and freeze for at least three hours.

4. Subsequently, cut into squares of the size of your preference.

NUTRITIONAL VALUES:

- Fat: 34g
- Carbohydrates: 19g
- Fiber: 7g
- Sugar: 9g
- Protein: 13g

CHIA PUDDING WITH BLUEBERRIES

Servings: 2

INGREDIENTS:

- 1 cup blueberries
- 1/4 cup chia seeds
- 1 and a half cups unsweetened almond and coconut milk
- 110g soft tofu
- 1/2 teaspoon pure almond extract
- 1/4 cup sliced almonds

INSTRUCTIONS:

1. Combine the almond milk, tofu, and almond extract very well with the help of a food processor.
2. Transfer the blend to a bowl, add the chia seeds, and stir to combine. Let rest for 10 minutes.
3. Heat a small pan over medium-low heat, add sliced almonds, and stir until lightly toasted. Remove from heat and reserve.
4. Gently add the blueberries to the chia mix and refrigerate.
5. Evenly distribute the chilled mixture into four small bowls and garnish with the toasted almonds. You can add more blueberries if you want.

NUTRITIONAL VALUES:

- Calories: 225 kcal
- Fat: 13 g
- Carbohydrates: 21 g
- Fiber: 14 g
- Protein: 11 g

CHOCOLATE PECAN BUTTER SHAKE

Servings: 2

INGREDIENTS:

- 1 tablespoon organic cocoa powder
- 1 tablespoon chocolate protein powder
- 1 medium frozen banana
- 1 cup plain, fat-free kefir
- 2 tablespoons nuts (such as almonds, pecans, or walnuts)
- 1 cup raw spinach
- Ice cubes
- Water

INSTRUCTIONS:

1. Add all the ingredients to a blender.
2. Add more or less ice or water, depending on the desired consistency.
3. Mix quickly until the liquid reaches a smooth consistency.

NUTRITIONAL VALUES:

- Calories: 260
- Protein: 16g
- Fat: 12g
- Carbohydrates: 30g
- Fiber: 7g

PINEAPPLE AND TURMERIC SMOOTHIE

Servings: 1

INGREDIENTS:

- 1 cup almond or coconut milk
- 1 cup fresh or frozen pineapple
- 1 cup unsweetened coconut milk yogurt
- 1 tsp ground turmeric
- 1 tsp honey
- Pinch of black pepper (optional)

INSTRUCTIONS:

1. Mix everything in a high-speed mixer.
2. Sip and enjoy!

NUTRITIONAL VALUES:

- Calories: 250
- Protein: 5g
- Fat: 10g
- Carbohydrates: 36g
- Fiber: 5g

BLUEBERRY COCOA SMOOTHIE FOR BREAKFAST

Servings: 1

INGREDIENTS:

- 1/2 cup unsweetened whole coconut milk
- 1/2 cup unsweetened almond milk
- 1 cup frozen blueberries
- 1 tablespoon raw cocoa beans
- 1 tablespoon almond butter
- 1 tablespoon unsweetened cocoa powder (optional)
- 1 cup fresh or frozen spinach (optional)
- Ice, to taste

INSTRUCTIONS:

1. Add everything to a blender and beat until creamy.

NUTRITIONAL VALUES:

- Calories: 308
- Fat: 22.1g
- Carbohydrates: 27.7g
- Fiber: 9.7g
- Protein: 8.8g

RISE & SHINE GREEN SMOOTHIE

Servings: 2

INGREDIENTS:

- 1 cup unsweetened almond milk
- 1 frozen banana
- 1/2 ripe avocado, sliced (fresh or frozen)
- 1 handful of spinach, fresh or frozen
- 1-3 teaspoons of pure maple syrup or raw honey
- 1 tablespoon ground flax seeds

INSTRUCTIONS:

1. Throw it all in the blender and whip up this ultimate green smoothie until smooth and creamy. Pour into a glass, sip, and enjoy.

NUTRITIONAL VALUES:

- Calories: 185
- Protein: 4g
- Fat: 11g
- Carbohydrates: 22g
- Fiber: 6g

RASPBERRY CHIA
ANTI-INFLAMMATORY SMOOTHIE

Servings: 2

INGREDIENTS:

- 1 cup unsweetened almond milk
- 1 tablespoon almond butter
- 2 teaspoons chia seeds
- 1 cup frozen raspberries
- 2 teaspoons ground flaxseed
- 1 scoop vanilla protein powder
- 1-2 teaspoons manuka honey (optional)

INSTRUCTIONS:

1. Add everything to a blender and beat until smooth. Taste it and adjust the toppings as you like. Serve and enjoy.

NUTRITIONAL VALUES:

- Calories: 217
- Total Fat: 11g
- Total Carbohydrates: 23g
- Fiber: 12g
- Protein: 16g

AVOCADO MINT COCOA SMOOTHIE

Servings: 2

INGREDIENTS:

- 1 cup unsweetened almond milk
- 1 frozen banana
- 1/2 ripe avocado, fresh or frozen
- 1 handful of fresh mint leaves
- 1-2 tablespoons pure maple syrup or raw honey
- 1 tablespoon raw cacao nibs
- 1-2 tablespoons cocoa powder (optional)

INSTRUCTIONS:

1. Put all the ingredients in a high-speed mixer and beat until smooth.
2. Enjoy as a refreshing breakfast or mid-day snack.

NUTRITIONAL VALUES:

- Calories: 228
- Fat: 12.2g
- Carbohydrates: 30.7g
- Fiber: 7.7g
- Protein: 3.9g

WHOLEMEAL BUN WITH RADISH COTTAGE CHEESE AND PEAR

Servings: 2

INGREDIENTS:

- 6 radishes, thinly sliced
- 2 spring onions, thinly sliced
- 200g cottage cheese (10% fat in dry matter)
- 1 tsp mustard
- 1 tbsp lemon juice
- Salt
- Pepper
- 50g arugula
- 2 pears, sliced
- 2 whole grain bread rolls

INSTRUCTIONS:

1. Clean and wash the radishes and cut them into small strips or cubes. Clean and wash the spring onions and cut them into very fine rings. Mix radishes with green onions, cottage cheese, mustard, and lemon juice, and season with pepper and salt.

2. Wash the rocket and shake it dry. Wash the pear, half, and core and cut into wedges.

3. Cut the rolls open, top them with the rocket, spread with the spread, and put the pear slices on top.

NUTRITIONAL VALUES:

- Calories: 380
- Protein: 20g
- Fat: 7g
- Carbohydrates: 62g
- Fiber: 12g

FLAX PUDDING

Servings: 2

INGREDIENTS:

- 4 tbsp ground flaxseed
- 300ml almond drink (almond milk) or another plant-based milk alternative
- 1 banana
- 1 apple
- 1 pinch cinnamon powder

INSTRUCTIONS:

1. Mix the ground flaxseed with the almond drink and place in the fridge overnight.
2. The next morning, peel and slice the banana. Wash, quarter, core, and slice the apples.
3. Stir flaxseed pudding and fill into 2 cereal bowls. Garnish with fruit and sprinkle with cinnamon.

NUTRITIONAL VALUES:

- Calories: 234
- Protein: 6g
- Fat: 11g
- Carbohydrates: 30g
- Fiber: 12g

RYE BREAD WITH AVOCADO AND BEETROOT SPREAD

Servings: 4

INGREDIENTS:

- 125g small beetroot (2 small; pre-cooked, vacuumed)
- 250g chickpeas (can; drained weight)
- 4 tbsp olive oil
- Salt
- Pepper
- 200g wholegrain rye bread (4 slices)
- 2 avocados
- 15g toasted sesame (1 tbsp)

INSTRUCTIONS:

1. Cut the beets into small cubes. Finely puree the beetroot cubes, chickpeas, oil, salt, and pepper with a hand blender.
2. Toast the bread slices and spread with beetroot spread. Halve the avocados, remove the stone, remove the flesh from the skin, and cut them into slices. Arrange the avocado slices in a fan shape on the bread and sprinkle with sesame seeds.

NUTRITIONAL VALUES:

- Calories: 324
- Fat: 20g
- Saturated Fat: 3g
- Carbohydrates: 27g
- Fiber: 9g

RED SMOOTHIE BOWL WITH STRAWBERRIES

Servings: 4

INGREDIENTS:

- 1kg watermelon (about 0.25 watermelons)
- 500g strawberries
- 1 orange
- 2 stems mint
- 1 tbsp maple syrup
- 60g oatmeal (4 tbsp)
- 15g raisins (1 tbsp)
- 60g almond kernels (4 tbsp)

INSTRUCTIONS:

1. Peel the melon and roughly dice the flesh. Wash and trim strawberries. Quarter half of the berries and set aside for the garnish.

2. Halve the orange and squeeze the juice. Wash the mint, shake it dry, and pluck off the leaves. Halve the remaining strawberries and puree finely in a blender with pieces of melon, orange juice, and maple syrup.

3. Pour the puree into 4 bowls and garnish with rolled oats and raisins. Roughly chop the almonds and sprinkle them on top. Garnish with the remaining strawberries and mint leaves. Serve immediately.

NUTRITIONAL VALUES:

- Calories: 284
- Protein: 8g
- Fat: 11g
- Carbohydrates: 41g Fiber: 7g

QUINOA WITH CHOCOLATE AND COCONUT

Servings: 2

INGREDIENTS:

- 75g quinoa
- 1 apple, cored and chopped
- 150ml coconut milk
- 2 tsp honey
- 2 tbsp linseed
- 1 tbsp cocoa powder
- Salt
- Walnuts (optional)
- Dark chocolate (optional)
- Coconut flakes (optional)
- Fruit (optional)

INSTRUCTIONS:

1. Rinse the quinoa in a colander under hot water. Then put in a saucepan with 150ml of water and boil. Cover and simmer for about 15 minutes. Meanwhile, dice or slice the apple.

2. Add the coconut milk, honey, flaxseed, cocoa powder, and salt to the quinoa, heat over low heat, and stir well.

3. Divide breakfast quinoa between 2 small bowls and garnish with nuts, chocolate,

coconut flakes, and fruit as desired.

NUTRITIONAL VALUES:

- Calories: 385
- Protein: 8g
- Fat: 20g
- Carbohydrates: 47g
- Fiber: 7g

VEGETABLE MUESLI
WITH FLAKED ALMONDS

Servings: 2

INGREDIENTS:

- 250g cucumber (about 0.5 cucumbers)
- Salt
- 75g 5-grain flakes
- 10g flaked almonds (1 tbsp)
- 1 yellow pepper
- 240g tomatoes (about 3 tomatoes)
- 2 stems basil
- 200g yoghurt (1.5% fat)
- Pepper

INSTRUCTIONS:

1. Wash the cucumber thoroughly and rub it dry. Halve lengthwise, deseed with a teaspoon, and cut into small cubes.

2. Place the cucumber cubes in a bowl and lightly salt. Mix with the cereal flakes and leave to infuse.

3. Roast the flaked almonds in a hot pan without fat over medium heat for 3 minutes and cool.

4. Quarter the peppers, deseed, wash, and cut them into fine strips.

5. Wash the tomatoes and cut out the stalks in a wedge shape. Quarter the tomatoes deseed and also cut them into fine strips.

6. Fold the tomato and pepper strips into the cucumber and flake mixture. Wash and shake dry the basil.

7. Pluck off the basil leaves, put a few aside, finely chop the rest and stir into the yogurt with a little pepper. Serve the vegetable muesli with the yogurt, sprinkle with almonds, and garnish with the remaining basil.

NUTRITIONAL VALUES:

- Calories: 309
- Protein: 13g
- Fat: 8g
- Carbohydrates: 51g
- Fiber: 14g

VITAMIN CRACKERS

Servings: 2

INGREDIENTS:

- 3 large carrots
- 150g cream cheese (double cream)
- 1 pinch salt
- 1/2 tsp honey
- 4 wholemeal crispbread discs
- 2 tsp chopped parsley
- 8 walnut halves

INSTRUCTIONS:

1. Clean, wash and grate the carrots, mix half of them into the cream cheese, and season to taste with salt and honey.

2. Spread it over the crispbreads and spread the remaining grated carrots over it. Garnish with parsley and walnut halves.

NUTRITIONAL VALUES:

- Calories: 323
- Protein: 10g
- Fat: 22g
- Carbohydrates: 22g
- Fiber: 5g

SEMOLINA PORRIDGE

Servings: 2

INGREDIENTS:

- 40g wheat semolina
- 250ml organic milk (0.5%)
- 20g glucose
- 10g ginger root
- 3g lemon peel
- 2g vanilla
- 2g cinnamon

INSTRUCTIONS:

1. Put the milk in a pan and heat it. Grate ginger and lemon zest. It would be best if you used an untreated lemon. Stir the vanilla, cinnamon, and dextrose into the milk and bring the milk to a boil once.

2. Then remove the milk from the stove and set the stovetop to the lowest setting. Stir in the semolina and cook over low heat for 5 minutes while stirring.

3. Then let the porridge cool down for about 10 minutes.

NUTRITIONAL VALUES:

- Calories 159
- Protein 6.58g
- Carbohydrates 31.58g
- Fat 0.37g

LUNCH RECIPES

PASTA WITH BASIL SPIRULINA PESTO

Servings: 5

INGREDIENTS:

- 100g fresh basil
- 30g spirulina
- 40g roasted pine nuts
- 50g rapeseed oil
- 50g olive oil
- 2 tsp salt (10g)
- 70g young Gouda cheese
- 2 garlic cloves (6g)
- 500g spelt tagliatelle
- 2 liters water (2000g)

INSTRUCTIONS:

1. Heat two liters of water in a large saucepan, salt with 1.5 teaspoons of salt, and add the spelled noodles to the boiling water. Put the lid on and cook the noodles for 8-12 minutes, depending on the instructions.

2. Meanwhile, place the pine nuts in a small pan and toast them over medium-high heat until lightly browned.

3. Wash and dry 2 bunches of basil. Peel garlic cloves.

4. Put the pine nuts, basil, garlic cloves, olive oil, rapeseed oil, spirulina powder, and some salt in a tall container and mash with a hand blender until you get a creamy pesto.

5. Chop the gouda as finely as possible with a cheese grater or a knife. Drain the pasta and mix it with the basil and spirulina pesto. Arrange on plates and sprinkle over the gouda. If you tolerate it and like it, add some pepper.

NUTRITIONAL VALUES:

- Calories 634
- Protein 18.53g
- Carbohydrates 72.54g
- Fat 29.76g

LEMON CHICKEN WITH QUINOA PEPPER SALAD

Servings: 2

INGREDIENTS:

- 250g organic chicken breast
- 1 organic lemon (50g)
- 100g quinoa
- 1 yellow bell pepper (150g)
- 1 red bell pepper (150g)
- 1 zucchini (300g)
- 100g chickpeas (jar/can)
- 4 tbsp (30g) virgin olive oil
- 1g dried thyme
- 2 tbsp (15g) balsamic vinegar
- 1 tsp (5g) salt
- 1g pepper

INSTRUCTIONS:

1. Grate 1 teaspoon of lemon zest and squeeze lemon halves. Rinse the chicken breast fillets, pat dry, place in a freezer bag with the lemon juice and salt and pepper, knead well and marinate in the fridge for at least 20 minutes.

2. Cook quinoa in salted water according to package instructions. Drain the chickpeas, wash the peppers and courgettes, deseed the peppers, and cut both into small pieces (1 to 1.5 cm). Add the chickpeas, peppers, and zucchini to the quinoa for the last 8 minutes and cook. Then let it cool down for at least 10 minutes.

3. Heat the oil over a medium-high pan, sear the chicken breasts on each side for 5 to 6 minutes, and season with salt, pepper, and thyme. Let cool down.

4. Mix the vegetables, chickpeas, quinoa, thyme, and balsamic vinegar. Thickly slice the lemon chicken, serve with the quinoa salad, and place in a carrier.

NUTRITIONAL VALUES:

- Calories 553
- Protein 41.83g
- Carbohydrates 48.32g
- Fat 20.27g

QUICK LENTIL TURMERIC BOWL

Servings: 2

INGREDIENTS:

- 130g lentil turmeric porridge
- 400g water
- 1 red bell pepper (150g)
- 1 avocado (250g)
- 2 branches/10g fresh basil
- 2 tbsp (16g) balsamic vinegar
- 2 tbsp (16g) virgin olive oil
- 1/2 spring onion (30g)

INSTRUCTIONS:

1. Put the lentils turmeric porridge with 400ml water in a saucepan, boil, and simmer for 3 minutes.
2. Microwave (without cooking)
3. Mix the porridge with water and heat in the microwave for about 1.5 minutes (at 600w).
4. Meanwhile, wash and remove the basil from the stems.
5. Halve, deseed, and remove the avocado from the skin.
6. Wash the peppers, deseed, and cut them into bite-sized cubes or fine strips. Wash the spring onion and cut it into fine rings.
7. Divide the finished lentil turmeric porridge between 2 bowls and garnish with the diced peppers, spring onions, avocado & basil. Then drizzle with 1 tablespoon each of olive oil and balsamic vinegar, and your quick takeaway meal is ready!

NUTRITIONAL VALUES:

- Calories 483
- Protein 11.33g
- Carbohydrates 45.00g
- Fat 27.21g

ZUCCHINI NOODLES WITH WILD GARLIC PESTO

Servings: 2

INGREDIENTS:

- 3 zucchini (600g)
- 10 cherry tomatoes (120g)
- 50g pine nuts
- 150g wild garlic
- 1/2 tsp (2.5g) sea salt
- 80g cashews
- 3 tbsp (25g) virgin olive oil

INSTRUCTIONS:

1. Soak the cashews in water overnight or simmer them in the pot for 15 minutes.
2. For the zucchini noodles, wash them zucchini and use a spiralizer to cut them into zoodles.
3. Place zucchini noodles in a colander and rinse with hot water for a few seconds.
4. Wash and halve the cherry tomatoes.
5. For the wild garlic pesto, use a hand blender to puree the soaked cashews with wild garlic, salt, olive oil, and lemon juice to form a pesto. Add a little more olive oil if needed.
6. Serve the zucchini noodles with fresh wild garlic pesto, cherry tomatoes, and pine nuts.

NUTRITIONAL VALUES:

- Calories578
- Protein 21.74g
- Carbohydrates21.25g
- Fat45.23g

ASIA POINTED TO CABBAGE EDAMAME PAN

Servings: 3

INGREDIENTS:

- 1 cabbage (1000g)
- 200g edamame (frozen)
- 3 vine tomatoes (600g)
- 1 onion (100g)
- 3 tbsp (30g) tomato paste
- 3 tbsp (25g) olive oil
- 180g vegan sausages
- 2 tsp (4g) turmeric
- 2 tsp (6g) whole grain black cumin
- 1 tsp (3g) salt
- 1g pepper

INSTRUCTIONS:

1. Remove the leaves of the pointed cabbage. Quarter the cabbage cut it into strips, and wash.
2. Peel and chop the onion. Wash and dice the tomato.
3. Cut vegan sausages into bite-sized pieces.
4. Heat oil in a large pan, add onion, and sauté for 2 minutes.
5. Add the pointed cabbage, reduce the heat slightly, and fry for about 5 minutes. Stir occasionally.
6. Add edamame and cook for another 5 minutes until the cabbage is done.
7. Add the tomato pieces, turmeric, vegan sausages, and tomato paste, mix well, season with salt and pepper, and continue to simmer for 2 - 3 minutes.
8. Arrange on plates and sprinkle with black cumin.

NUTRITIONAL VALUES:

- Calories 482
- Protein 24.62g
- Carbohydrates 28.23g
- Fat 29.59g

SWEDISH MILK POTATO VEGETABLE SOUP

Servings: 2

INGREDIENTS:

- 400g potatoes
- 1 cucumber (550g)
- 15 radishes (175g)
- 10g fresh dill
- 10g fresh parsley
- 500ml Swedish milk
- 2 tbsp (16g) chia oil
- 300ml water
- 3g salt
- 1g black pepper

INSTRUCTIONS:

1. For the cold Swedish milk soup, peel the potatoes, wash them, and cut them into small cubes. Bring salted water to a boil in a saucepan and cook the potato pieces in it for 20 minutes. Drain and let cool.

2. In the meantime, wash the radishes and cucumbers thoroughly and dice finely. Wash, dry, and finely chop the dill and parsley.

3. Mix Swedish milk with chia oil, cold water, and lightly salt and pepper. Stir in the radishes, cucumber, parsley, dill, and the cooled potato pieces, and refrigerate until ready to serve. The healthy probiotic meal with Swedish milk is ready. Bon appetit.

NUTRITIONAL VALUES:

- Calories 436
- Protein 15.41g
- Carbohydrates 50.85g
- Fat 17.52g

VEGAN SHEPHERD'S PIE

Servings: 4

INGREDIENTS:

- 1kg sweet potato
- 100ml soy milk
- 2 tbsp (24g) vegetable margarine
- 1g grated nutmeg
- 200g lentils
- 1 onion (82g)
- 2 garlic cloves (6g)
- 2 carrots (124g)
- 100g fresh celery
- 200g mushrooms
- 150ml vegetable broth
- 2 tbsp (30g) tomato paste
- 2 tbsp (28g) balsamic vinegar
- 4 tbsp (32g) rapeseed oil
- 3 branches/10g fresh thyme
- 1 tsp (1g) dried cumin
- 3g salt
- 1g pepper

INSTRUCTIONS:

1. For the sweet potato layer: wash, peel, and dice sweet potatoes. Cook in boiling salted water for about 15-20 minutes until tender.

2. Drain off the cooking water, and put the potatoes back in the pot. Add the margarine, soy milk, and nutmeg and mash everything with a potato masher to a puree. Season with salt and pepper and set aside.

3. For the lentil and mushroom filling, cook the lentils according to the package instructions.

4. Meanwhile, prepare the vegetables: wash, peel, and finely chop the carrots. Also, peel and chop the onion and garlic. Wash and finely chop the celery. Clean and roughly chop the mushrooms.

5. Heat rapeseed oil in a pan. Add onion & garlic and sauté 2 minutes.

6. Detach the thyme from the sprigs.

7. Add the carrots, celery, mushrooms, thyme, and cumin to the pan and sauté for about 5 minutes.

8. Add tomato paste, balsamic vinegar, cooked lentils, and vegetable stock, and boil. Simmer over low heat for 5 to 10 minutes until most liquid evaporates. If necessary, season with salt & pepper.

9. Place the lentil and mushroom filling in a casserole dish and cover it with mashed sweet potatoes.

10. Bake the vegan shepherd's pie at 200°c for 20 minutes.

NUTRITIONAL VALUES:

- Calories 590
- Protein 19.93g
- Carbohydrates 87.59g
- Fat 16.67g

CORN SOUP WITH CHIA SEEDS

Servings: 4

INGREDIENTS:

- 300g corn
- 1 onion (82g)
- 1 garlic clove (3g)
- 1/2 chili (2.5g)
- 1 tsp (1g) turmeric
- 1 can (400g) coconut milk
- 10g fresh parsley
- 1 tbsp (6g) lemon juice
- 1 tbsp (8g) chia seeds
- 1 tbsp (8g) olive oil
- 5g salt
- 2g pepper

INSTRUCTIONS:

1. Chop the onion, garlic, and chili into fine strips. Heat olive oil in a saucepan and sauté onion, garlic, and chili for 2-3 minutes.
2. Roast the turmeric and curry for about 1 minute. Add the corn.
3. Deglaze with vegetable broth and coconut milk and bring to a boil. Simmer for about 10 minutes over medium heat. Stir now and then.
4. Meanwhile, wash, chop, and set aside the parsley.
5. Puree the soup with a hand blender until a creamy mass is formed. Season with lemon juice, salt, and pepper.
6. Divide corn soup between plates, garnish with chia seeds and parsley, and you're done!

NUTRITIONAL VALUES:

- Calories325
- Protein 5.07g
- Carbohydrates17.21
- Fat 25.65g

AVOCADO SALAD WITH CHICKPEAS

Servings: 2

INGREDIENTS:

- 1 can (400g) chickpeas
- 1 ready-to-eat avocado (160g)
- 50g feta cheese
- 1 tbsp (8g) olive oil
- 2 branches/5g fresh parsley
- 1/2 organic lemon (45g)
- 2g salt
- 1/2 cucumber (200g)

INSTRUCTIONS:

1. Drain, rinse, and drain the chickpeas. Halve, deseed, peel, and dice the avocado.
2. Wash cucumber. Also, dice feta and cucumber. Mix everything in a bowl.
3. Roughly chop the parsley and add it.
4. Squeeze lemon. Mix juice with balsamic vinegar, olive oil, and salt and pour over the avocado salad. Complete!

NUTRITIONAL VALUES:

- Calories 514
- Protein 20.88g
- Carbohydrates 48.24g
- Fat 25.77g

VEGETABLE STIR-FRY

Servings: 2

INGREDIENTS:

- 1 broccoli (347g)
- 3 carrots (186g)
- 1 yellow bell pepper (155g)
- 1 red bell pepper (155g)
- 3 branches/60g spring onions
- 1 garlic clove (3g)
- 10g ginger
- 1 chili pepper (5g)
- 4 tbsp (60g) soy sauce
- 2 tbsp (20g) sesame oil
- 3 tbsp (24g) rapeseed oil
- 1 tbsp (15g) miso paste
- 2g salt
- 1g pepper

INSTRUCTIONS:

1. Clean the peppers and cut them into thin slices. Wash the broccoli and cut the florets into bite-sized pieces. Peel the carrots, halve lengthways, and cut them into thin strips.

2. Clean the spring onions and chop them into fine rings. Wash the chili, cut it into thin rings, and remove the seeds. Peel garlic. Ginger peel and finely chop.

3. Heat rapeseed oil in a wok. Briefly sauté the spring onions, chili, and ginger, and press the garlic. Add the broccoli, carrots, peppers, and sauté for 5-10 minutes.

4. Dissolve the miso paste in water, add to the pan, and simmer for 2 minutes. Add the soy sauce and sesame oil and season with salt and pepper. Suitable without supplements for healthy weight loss. Rice, quinoa, or Asian mi noodles go well with this.

NUTRITIONAL VALUES:

- Calories 375
- Protein 13.21g
- Carbohydrates 26.71g
- Fat 23.75g

CHICKPEA TUNA SALAD

Servings: 2

INGREDIENTS:

- 1 can (195g) tuna
- 1 can (265g) chickpeas
- 1 red onion (82g)
- 3 branches/30g fresh parsley
- 2 tsp (10g) mustard
- 2 tsp (20g) honey
- 1 1/2 tbsp (12g) olive oil
- 1 tbsp (8g) balsamic vinegar
- 2g salt

INSTRUCTIONS:

1. Drain the tuna and chickpeas. Mash the tuna lightly with a fork.
2. Finely dice the onions, chop the parsley, and mix with the tuna and chickpeas in a bowl.
3. Mix the mustard, honey, olive oil, balsamic vinegar, and salt for the dressing and pour over the salad. This goes well with delicious bread.

NUTRITIONAL VALUES:

- Calories 396
- Protein 33.72g
- Carbohydrates 40.65g
- Fat 10.33g

MILLET AND BEAN PATTIES

Servings: 3

INGREDIENTS:

- Millet: 100 grams
- Oatmeal: 60 grams
- Black bean: 1 can / 240 grams
- Onion: 1 piece / 82 grams
- Flaxseed (crushed): 2 tablespoons / 14 grams
- Tomato paste: 1 tablespoon / 15 grams
- Salt: 1 teaspoon / 5 grams
- Paprika powder: 1 teaspoon / 1 gram
- Parsley (fresh): 15 grams
- Olive oil: 4 tablespoons / 32 grams

INSTRUCTIONS:

1. Wash millet and boil with 2.5 times the amount of water. Simmer for about 15 minutes and let swell for 15 minutes. Note: the preparation may vary; follow the instructions on the pack.

2. Mix the flaxseed with 2 tablespoons of water and let it swell.

3. Finely dice the onions and sauté briefly in olive oil.

4. Briefly put the oat flakes in a blender until a coarse flour is formed. Drain the beans and mash them with a potato masher to a chewy mass. You can leave some of the black beans whole for the look if you like. Mix the bean mixture with the oatmeal.

5. Add onions, swollen flax seeds, spices, chopped parsley, salt, tomato paste, and finally, the millet, and mix everything.

6. Form about 12 patties from the mixture and fry in a pan on both sides in olive oil until golden brown. Serve with a salad or vegetables.

NUTRITIONAL VALUES:

- Calories 388
- Protein 11.86g
- Carbohydrates 47.30g
- Fat 15.54g

PROTEIN LEGUMES PAN

Servings: 2

INGREDIENTS:

- Borlotti bean (jar): 200 grams
- Peas (frozen): 200 grams
- Chickpeas (jar/can): 170 grams
- Lentils (tin/jar): 150 grams
- Rapeseed oil: 4 tablespoons / 40 grams
- Broccoli: 250 grams
- Mushrooms: 200 grams
- Soy sauce (gluten-free): 20 grams
- Pepper: 3 grams
- Cumin (dried): 2 teaspoons / 4 grams
- Coriander (ground): 3 grams

INSTRUCTIONS:

1. Rinse the broccoli briefly with cold water and shake dry. Cut off the florets and remove woody parts and leaves from the stalk. Cut the florets and stalk into small pieces. Clean the mushrooms and cut them into slices.
2. Heat rapeseed oil (or olive oil) in a pan, add Borlotti beans, peas, lentils, and chickpeas, and cook for 5 minutes.
3. Add the broccoli and mushrooms and continue cooking for 5 minutes.
4. Season the protein and legume pan generously with coriander, cumin, pepper, and soy sauce and serve hot.

NUTRITIONAL VALUES:

- Calories 550
- Protein 32.60g
- Carbohydrates 48.36g
- Fat 23.46g

PUMPKIN SWEET POTATO SKILLET

Servings: 4

INGREDIENTS:

- Hokkaido pumpkin: 1 piece / 1000 grams
- Sweet potato: 2 pieces / 600 grams
- Corn: 1 can / 150 grams
- Kidney beans (can): 1 can / 400 grams
- Chili pepper/s: 2 pieces / 8 grams
- Olive oil: 5 tablespoons / 50 grams
- Salt: 4 grams
- Cumin (dried): 1 gram
- Parsley (fresh): 15 grams

INSTRUCTIONS:

1. Wash the Hokkaido squash and place the whole on a baking sheet in the oven. So it becomes soft for cutting. Bake at 150 degrees for 15-25 minutes. Let the pre-cooked Hokkaido cool down, cut it in half, and remove the seeds with a spoon. The Hokkaido does not need to be peeled. Cut the squash into wedges, then into 1-1.5 cm pieces.

2. While the squash is in the oven, peel and wash the sweet potatoes. Cut the sweet potatoes into 1 cm pieces.

3. Heat 5 tbsp oil in a large pan. Fry the sweet potato and pumpkin over medium heat for 15-20 minutes, turning occasionally.

4. Wash and dry the parsley, remove the stalks, chop, and set aside.

5. Remove the seeds from the chilies, chop finely, and add to the pan. Drain the kidney beans and corn in a colander,

rinse with water, add to the pan, and heat briefly. Season the pumpkin and sweet potato pan with salt and cumin and remove from the heat.

6. Stir in the parsley, arrange the pumpkin and sweet potato pan on plates, and serve hot.

NUTRITIONAL VALUES:

- Calories 483
- Protein 16.03g
- Carbohydrates 69.49g
- Fat 14.85g

CRUNCHY LAMB'S LETTUCE WITH BLUEBERRIES AND HEMP SEEDS

Servings: 1

INGREDIENTS:

- Lamb's lettuce: 100 grams
- Blueberries: 80 grams
- Mushrooms: 100 grams
- Hemp seeds (shelled): 2 tablespoons / 20 grams
- Cane sugar: 1 teaspoon / 5 grams
- Lime juice: 2 tablespoons / 15 grams
- Linseed oil (native, organic): 1 tablespoon / 12 grams
- Salt: 3 grams
- Black pepper (freshly ground): 2 grams

INSTRUCTIONS:

1. Wash and dry the lamb's lettuce and blueberries thoroughly. Clean and slice champions.
2. For the dressing: measure out the lime juice (2 tablespoons) and mix the cane sugar, linseed oil, pepper, and salt. Gently mix the dressing into the salad.
3. Mix all ingredients (hemp seeds, lamb's lettuce, champions, blueberries, and dressing) and arrange on a plate.

NUTRITIONAL VALUES:

- Calories 326
- Protein 13.30g
- Carbohydrates 16.74g
- Fat 22.61g

ORANGE AND WALNUT SALAD

Servings: 2

INGREDIENTS:

- Radicchio: 200 grams
- Endive: 200 grams
- Orange: 2 pieces / 300 grams
- Walnuts: 50 grams
- Omega-3 dha+epa oil: 3 tablespoons / 20 grams
- Vinegar: 1 tablespoon / 10 grams
- Mild mustard: 1 teaspoon / 10 grams
- Horseradish paste: 1 teaspoon / 6 grams
- Sugar beet syrup: 1 teaspoon / 10 grams
- Salt: 1 teaspoon / 5 grams

INSTRUCTIONS:

1. Wash the lettuce and drain well, ideally dry in a salad spinner. Chop the lettuce leaves and place them in a salad bowl.

2. Peel and fillet the oranges and add the roughly chopped walnuts to the bowl.

3. In a tightly sealable jar, stir the molasses, horseradish, mustard, salt, and vinegar together. Add oil. Close the jar and shake vigorously. Pour the salad dressing over the salad, mix, and serve immediately.

NUTRITIONAL VALUES:

- Calories 381
- Protein 8.93g
- Carbohydrates 20.68g
- Fat 28.53g

HEALTHY FALAFEL

Servings: 2

INGREDIENTS:

- Chickpeas (dried): 225 grams
- Spring onion: 4 pieces / 80 grams
- Garlic cloves: 3 pieces / 9 grams
- Parsley (fresh): 5 branches / 60 grams
- Coriander (fresh): 3 branches / 30 grams
- Peppermint (fresh): 2 branches / 20 grams
- Ground caraway: 1 teaspoon / 1 gram
- Coriander (ground): 1 teaspoon / 1 gram
- Salt: 1 teaspoon / 5 grams
- Black pepper (freshly ground): 1 teaspoon / 1 gram
- Rapeseed oil (refined): 100 milliliters

INSTRUCTIONS:

1. Falafel only works with dried chickpeas soaked in plenty of water overnight. They should triple in size. The next day, drain the chickpeas well and place them in a blender.

2. Wash and roughly chop fresh herbs. Add the chickpeas with the spices and knead into a dough. That takes some patience. Stop the blender halfway through and scrape any mixture that has spilled up from the sides so that everything is evenly blended. The falafel batter is ready when it holds its shape.

3. Carefully form 18 falafels from the dough and fry them one after the other in hot oil.

4. Falafel can be prepared in a pot, pan, or oven without a deep fryer!

5. Pot: heat 400ml rapeseed oil in a high saucepan to around 175 degrees. Carefully place the falafel in the pot, cook for 4 minutes, and lift out.

6. Pan: falafel also works well in a pan with lots of oil. The bottom of the pan must be covered (100ml) and set on the highest setting. A falafel from the pan takes about 10 minutes to turn.

7. Oven: falafel is lower in fat when baked in the oven. They become a little less crispy but still taste delicious. Preheat the oven to 190 °c, place the falafel on the baking tray, and brush all sides with 40 ml rapeseed oil. Bake in the hot oven for about 30 minutes. The falafel is done when they are lightly browned

8. Served with yogurt, mint sauce, salad, and hummus.

NUTRITIONAL VALUES:

- Calories 561
- Protein 15.85g
- Carbohydrates 38.93g
- Fat 38.14g

QUINOA SALAD WITH FETA

Servings: 2

INGREDIENTS:

- Quinoa: 150 grams
- Aubergine: 1 piece / 340 grams
- Feta (goat milk): 75 grams
- Arugula: 100 grams
- Garlic cloves: 1 piece / 3 grams
- Olive oil (virgin): 3 tablespoons / 24 grams
- Salt: 2 teaspoons / 10 grams
- Black pepper (freshly ground): 1 pinch / 1 gram
- Lemon juice: 1 tablespoon / 6 grams

INSTRUCTIONS:

1. Rinse the quinoa under running water. Bring 300ml of water to a boil with 1 teaspoon of salt. Bring the quinoa to a boil in salted water and simmer over low heat for about 15 minutes.

2. While the quinoa is simmering, wash and dice the aubergines. Put 2 tablespoons of oil in a non-stick pan and fry the aubergine cubes until the flesh is soft.

3. Wash the rocket, drain it, and cut it into small pieces. Peel and chop the garlic clove. Cut the feta into small cubes.

4. Place the quinoa in a bowl, and stir in the lemon juice and olive oil. Mix in the aubergine, feta cubes, rocket, and garlic, and season with salt and pepper. Leave to stand for an hour before serving.

NUTRITIONAL VALUES:

- Calories 533
- Carbohydrates 53.61g
- Protein 19.58g
- Fat 26.54g

SWEET POTATO PAN WITH HERBS & PAPRIKA

Servings: 3

INGREDIENTS:

- Sweet potato: 3 pieces / 930 grams
- Paprika: 2 pieces / 300 grams
- Spring onion: 4 pieces / 80 grams
- Garlic cloves: 2 pieces / 6 grams
- Parsley (fresh): 5 branches / 60 grams
- Garden herbs (frozen): 20 grams
- Salt: 1 tablespoon / 15 grams
- Olive oil: 4 tablespoons / 40 grams
- Pepper: 1 pinch / 1 gram

INSTRUCTIONS:

1. Cook the sweet potatoes in salted water for 10 minutes. Drain, peel, and cut into small cubes.

2. Wash the peppers, deseed, and cut them into fine strips. Wash the spring onions and cut them into rings. Peel and crush the garlic cloves. Wash and finely chop the parsley and herbs.

3. Heat oil in a pan. Fry sweet potatoes on medium flame. After 5 minutes of frying, mix in the spring onions, paprika, and garlic and cook for 8 minutes. Stir in the herbs at the end and season with salt and pepper.

NUTRITIONAL VALUES:

- Calories 513
- Protein 7.60g
- Carbohydrates 83.09g
- Fat 15.82g

SWEDE SOUP

Servings: 2

INGREDIENTS:

- Swedes: 1/2 piece / 500 grams
- Parsnips: 2 pieces / 250 grams
- Carrots: 2 pieces / 160 grams
- Garlic cloves: 1 piece / 3 grams
- Parsley (fresh): 5 branches / 60 grams
- Vegetable broth (gluten-free powder): 20 grams
- Onion: 1 piece / 60 grams
- Olive oil (virgin): 1 tablespoon / 10 grams

INSTRUCTIONS:

1. Peel the turnips, parsnips, and carrots and cut them into pieces. Finely chop the onion, and press the garlic.

2. Heat the oil in a saucepan, and cook the onion and garlic in the hot oil. Add the turnips, carrots, and parsnips, and fill with 1 liter of water. Stir in the vegetable broth.

3. Simmer the soup until the vegetables are soft, about 45 minutes. In the meantime, wash the parsley, pluck dry from the stalks, and chop finely. Stir in chopped parsley before serving.

NUTRITIONAL VALUES:

- Calories 263
- Protein 8.53g
- Carbohydrates 40.13g
- Fat 6.98g

SALAD WITH LENTILS AND SPELLED CROUTONS

Servings: 2

INGREDIENTS:

- Endive salad: 100 grams
- Arugula salad: 50 grams
- Radicchio: 50 grams
- Lentils (brown): 125 grams
- Water: 250 milliliters
- Spelt roll: 150 grams
- Apple cider vinegar: 1 tablespoon / 10 grams
- Rapeseed oil: 2 tablespoons / 20 grams
- Jam: 2 tablespoons / 20 grams
- Salt: 5 grams

INSTRUCTIONS:

1. Prepare the lentils in twice the amount of water according to the instructions on the package, add a little salt, and leave to cool.

2. Thoroughly wash the radicchio, endive, and rocket, dry (pat or spin), tear into bite-sized pieces, and place them in a salad bowl.

3. Mix the dressing with rapeseed oil, apple cider vinegar, jam, and some salt.

4. Cut the spelled rolls into slices, toast until crisp, and cut into cubes. If you don't have a toaster, you can toast the diced pieces of bread in the pan.

5. Stir the marinade and lentils into the salad before serving, then fold in the spelled croutons.

NUTRITIONAL VALUES:

- Calories 477
- Protein 23.97g
- Carbohydrates 62.43g

BRUSSELS SPROUTS WITH APPLE AND WALNUT

Servings: 2

INGREDIENTS:

- Cauliflower: 600 grams
- Rapeseed oil (refined): 1 tablespoon / 10 grams
- Apples: 2 pieces / 300 grams
- Onion: 2 pieces / 120 grams
- Walnuts: 50 grams
- Vegetable broth (powder): 1/2 teaspoon / 2 grams
- Water: 100 milliliters
- Salt: 1 teaspoon / 5 grams
- Pepper: 2 grams

INSTRUCTIONS:

1. Clean brussels sprouts, wash and quarter the florets. Peel the apples, and cut them into pieces. Peel and finely chop the onions.

2. Heat the oil in a pan and sauté the onions until translucent, stirring occasionally.

3. Add brussels sprouts and sauté briefly. Mix the vegetable stock in 100 ml of water, pour into the pan, and simmer over low heat for 15 minutes, stirring occasionally.

4. Chop the walnuts and stir in along with the apples. Just heat it and season the brussels sprouts pan with salt and pepper. Complete!

NUTRITIONAL VALUES:

- Calories 444
- Protein 18.85g
- Carbohydrates 36.51g

KOREAN BEAN SPROUTS SALAD

Servings: 2

INGREDIENTS:

- Bean sprouts (fresh): 250 grams
- Soy sauce: 2 teaspoons / 10 grams
- Sesame oil: 1 tablespoon / 8 grams
- Pear syrup: 2 tablespoons / 15 grams
- Roasted sesame: 1 tablespoon / 10 grams
- Salt: 3 grams
- Red chili powder: 1 gram

INSTRUCTIONS:

1. Wash the bean sprouts and blanch them in salted water, pour boiling water over them, and leave them to stand for 1 minute. Rinse and drain.
2. Mix soy sauce, sesame oil, salt, chili, and pear juice.
3. Mix the blanched soybean sprouts with the salad dressing, let stand for 1 minute and arrange on a plate - the delicious soybean sprouts salad is ready.

NUTRITIONAL VALUES:

- Calories 165
- Protein 9.57g
- Carbohydrates 12.96g
- Fat 8.24g

KOHLRABI SALAD

Servings: 2

INGREDIENTS:

- Kohlrabi: 1 piece / 265 grams
- Cucumber: 1 piece / 500 grams
- Apple: 1 piece / 150 grams
- Ginger (fresh): 5 grams
- Lemon juice: 35 grams
- Vinegar: 1 teaspoon / 5 grams
- Walnut oil: 3 tablespoons / 24 grams
- Parsley (fresh): 10 grams
- Salt: 1/2 teaspoon / 4 grams

INSTRUCTIONS:

1. Wash, peel, and coarsely grate the kohlrabi. Wash the cucumber, peel if you like, remove the seeds with a spoon, and grate coarsely.

2. Grate some fresh ginger. Wash the apple, peel it, grate it coarsely, and sprinkle it with the juice of one lemon.

3. Mix a salad dressing from vinegar, oil, salt, and parsley, and leave the kohlrabi salad in it for at least 15 minutes. Complete! Bon appétit!

NUTRITIONAL VALUES:

- Calories 226
- Protein 4.70g
- Carbohydrates 21.46g
- Fat 12.88g

ROASTED CHICKPEAS

Servings: 2

INGREDIENTS:

- Chickpeas (tin/jar): 1 can / 265 grams
- Rapeseed oil (tasteless): 2 tablespoons / 16 grams
- Sweet paprika: 1 teaspoon / 2 grams
- Turmeric: 1 teaspoon / 2 grams
- Ground caraway: 1 gram
- Cumin (dried): 1 gram
- Salt: 1/2 teaspoon / 3 grams

INSTRUCTIONS:

1. Put the chickpeas in a colander and rinse with water. Pat dry with paper towels to get them nice and crispy.
2. Put the dried chickpeas in a bowl with the rapeseed oil, salt, and spices, and mix.
3. Heat a pan and toast the chickpeas over medium heat for 15 to 20 minutes. Don't forget to stir from time to time. When the chickpeas are brown and crispy, decant and let cool slightly. Complete.
4. Tip: the spices can be changed as desired. The chickpea snack can also be sprinkled over salads or added to soups instead of croutons.

NUTRITIONAL VALUES:

- Calories 247
- Protein 10.07g
- Carbohydrates 24.39g
- Fat 11.89g

MATJES FILLETS ON WHOLEMEAL BREAD

Servings: 2

INGREDIENTS:

- Matjes (smoked): 300 grams
- Whole grain bread: 2 slices / 125 grams
- Butter: 10 grams
- Dill (fresh): 5 grams

INSTRUCTIONS:

1. Chop up herring fillet, fresh or from the refrigerated section (prepared with rapeseed oil), to the size of bread slices.
2. Slice wholemeal bread and spread with butter.
3. Serve the herring fillet on black bread. Decorate herring bread with dill.

NUTRITIONAL VALUES:

- Calories 578
- Protein 29.78g
- Carbohydrates 24.45g
- Fat 40.38g

HERRING SALAD
WITH CUCUMBER AND APPLE

Servings: 2

INGREDIENTS:

- Herring (smoked): 300 grams
- Onion: 1 piece / 50 grams
- Rapeseed oil (tasteless): 5 tablespoons / 40 grams
- Apple: 1 1/2 pieces / 150 grams
- Cucumber: 1 piece / 550 grams
- Dill (fresh): 5 grams
- Lemon juice: 3 tablespoons / 20 grams
- Apple cider vinegar: 2 tablespoons / 15 grams
- Salt: 4 grams
- Pepper: 1 gram
- Sugar: 1 teaspoon / 5 grams

INSTRUCTIONS:

1. Peel onions and cut them into fine pieces. Cut the herring into bite-sized pieces.
2. Clean the apple, cut it into quarters, cut the core into fine cubes, and sprinkle it with a little lemon juice.
3. Wash the cucumber, peel, and remove the seeds with a spoon, then cut them into fine cubes.
4. Whisk together the vinegar, rapeseed oil, salt, and pepper in a bowl. Flavor with lemon juice and sugar.
5. Mix all the ingredients for the herring salad in a bowl and mix with the dressing. Leave for at least 10 minutes and serve.

NUTRITIONAL VALUES:

- Calories 323
- Protein 15.54g
- Carbohydrates 10.17g
- Fat 24.37g

BEETROOT SALAD WITH WALNUTS

Servings: 2

INGREDIENTS:

- Beetroot (fresh): 400 grams
- Red onions: 1 piece / 50 grams
- Walnuts: 80 grams
- Thyme (fresh): 10 grams
- Linseed oil (native): 3 tablespoons / 25 grams
- Apple cider vinegar: 1 tablespoon / 12 grams
- Honey: 1 teaspoon / 5 grams
- Salt: 1/2 teaspoon / 3 grams
- Pepper: 2 grams

INSTRUCTIONS:

1. Roast walnuts in a pan.
2. Peel and dice the beetroot. Wash, dry, and pluck the thyme from the stems. Peel and finely chop the onion.
3. Mix the remaining ingredients (linseed oil, apple cider vinegar, honey, salt, and pepper) into a dressing and pour onto the walnut-beetroot mix.
4. Mix the beets, onions, roasted walnuts, and dressing, arrange them on plates, and decorate them with thyme. The beetroot salad is ready - without any apples!

NUTRITIONAL VALUES:

- Calories 501
- Protein 10.00g
- Carbohydrates 23.23g
- Fat 41.10g

KALE SALAD WITH EDAMAME AND CRANBERRIES

Servings: 2

INGREDIENTS:

- Kale (fresh): 300 grams
- Edamame (fresh): 200 grams
- Dried cranberries: 80 grams
- Cherry tomatoes: 10 pieces / 100 grams
- Olive oil (virgin): 4 tablespoons / 30 grams
- Lemon juice: 2 tablespoons / 15 grams
- Salt: 3 grams

INSTRUCTIONS:

1. Remove the stems from the kale, wash, dry, place in a bowl, and tear them into bite-sized pieces. Mix olive oil, salt, and lemon juice, pour over the kale, and knead the kale with your hands for 2 minutes until soft. It will also soften if you leave it covered and the dressing in the fridge for a few hours.

2. Place edamame in boiling water and cook until soft, 3 to 4 minutes. Drain in a colander, rinse with cold water, and leave to cool.

3. Meanwhile, wash and halve the tomatoes.

4. Add the cranberries, tomatoes, and edamame to the kale, stir, and season with salt and pepper. Complete!

NUTRITIONAL VALUES:

- Calories 468
- Protein 19.09g
- Carbohydrates 46.03g
- Fat 22.53g

KOHLRABI SOUP

Servings: 2

INGREDIENTS:

- Kohlrabi: 5 pieces / 1000 grams
- Potatoes: 2 pieces / 200 grams
- Shallot(s): 1 piece / 25 grams
- Olive oil: 3 tablespoons / 25 grams
- Water: 750 milliliters
- Vegetable broth (yeast-free, gluten-free, without glutamate): 1 teaspoon / 5 grams
- Seasoned salt: 2 grams
- Nutmeg (grated): 1 gram
- White pepper (powder): 1 gram
- Pimento: 1 gram
- Parsley (fresh): 10 grams

INSTRUCTIONS:

1. Wash the kohlrabi and potatoes, peel, and cut them into large pieces. Potatoes. Peel and finely chop the shallot. For light foods, omit the shallot

2. Heat the olive oil and sauté the shallot for 2 minutes. Add the kohlrabi and potatoes, stir, and sauté for 2 minutes. Add water and some vegetable stock, bring the kohlrabi soup to a boil, and cook for about 15 to 20 minutes.

3. Add spices. Puree the kohlrabi soup with a hand blender and season to taste. Chop the parsley and sprinkle over the kohlrabi soup when serving.

4. This kohlrabi soup without cream is particularly healthy: it is alkaline and is easy on the stomach and intestines (bland diet). Kohlrabi has a lot of selenium (especially as organic kohlrabi) and vitamin c. It has an anti-inflammatory effect and prevents cancer.

NUTRITIONAL VALUES:

- Calories 320
- Protein 12.18g
- Carbohydrates 35.77g
- Fat 13.64g

PAPRIKA RAW VEGETABLES WITH CASHEW DIP

Servings: 5

INGREDIENTS:

- Red paprika: 2 pieces / 300 grams
- Yellow paprika: 2 pieces / 300 grams
- Cucumber: 1 piece / 400 grams
- Carrots: 4 pieces / 200 grams
- Cashew cream: 5 tablespoons / 50 grams
- Natural yogurt (organic): 400 grams
- Fresh parsley: 25 grams
- Pepper: 1 gram

INSTRUCTIONS:

1. Peel the carrots and cucumber and wash the remaining vegetables. Halve the peppers, deseed, and cut them into strips 1-2 cm wide. Quarter the carrots and the cucumber, scrape off the seeds with a spoon, and cut into strips approx. 6 cm long. Drape raw vegetable slices in glasses.

2. For the cashew dip: stir together the cashew cream and yogurt. Season with salt and pepper. Cut the parsley or other herbs into fine rolls and mix them into the cashew dip.

NUTRITIONAL VALUES:

- Calories 187
- Protein 7.00g
- Carbohydrates 17.60g
- Fat 9.27g

PEPPER SALAD WITH KIDNEY BEANS

Servings: 4

INGREDIENTS:

- Yellow paprika: 2 pieces / 300 grams
- Red paprika: 2 pieces / 300 grams
- Green pepper: 1 piece / 155 grams
- Onion: 2 pieces / 130 grams
- Kidney beans: 1 can / 255 grams
- Hemp oil: 4 tablespoons / 40 grams
- Salt: 1 teaspoon / 5 grams
- Black pepper (freshly ground): 1 gram
- Sugar: 1 teaspoon / 5 grams
- Herbal vinegar: 1 tablespoon / 10 grams

INSTRUCTIONS:

1. Wash the peppers thoroughly, remove the stalk and seeds, and cut them into fine strips.

2. Peel the onions and cut them into small cubes or rings. Take the kidney beans out of the can, put them in a colander, rinse thoroughly, and drain.

3. For the dressing of the paprika salad, mix olive oil, salt, sugar, and pepper in a glass and add the herb vinegar at the end and stir in.

4. Mix the peppers, onions, kidney beans, and dressing in a large bowl and leave the pepper salad in the fridge for a while (at least 1 hour).

NUTRITIONAL VALUES:

- Calories 315
- Protein 16.80g
- Carbohydrates 36.16g
- Fat 11.57g

OVEN VEGETABLES MEDITERRANEAN

Servings: 2

INGREDIENTS:

- Zucchini: 2 pieces / 400 grams
- Paprika: 3 pieces / 450 grams
- Cherry tomatoes: 10 pieces / 100 grams
- Aubergine: 1/2 piece / 170 grams
- Onion: 1 piece / 80 grams
- Black olives (pickled, glass): 40 grams
- Garlic cloves: 1 piece / 4 grams
- Fresh thyme: 3 grams
- Fresh oregano: 5 grams
- Fresh basil: 10 grams
- Black pepper (freshly ground): 3 grams
- Olive oil: 4 tablespoons / 30 grams

INSTRUCTIONS:

1. Wash the vegetables. Wash the peppers and cut them into small pieces. Thinly slice the zucchini and aubergine. Peel onions and garlic. Finely chop the onion and garlic. Then wash and finely chop the herbs. Cut the olives into rings. The cherry tomatoes remain whole.

2. Place the oven vegetables in a large casserole dish or deep baking tray, add the herbs, and mix well with the olive oil.

3. Cook the Mediterranean oven vegetables in a preheated oven at 180 degrees for 25-30 minutes. Stir once in between. After baking, season the oven vegetables with salt and pepper and serve.

NUTRITIONAL VALUES:

- Calories 300
- Protein 9.36g
- Carbohydrates 19.25g
- Fat 20.10g

AUBERGINE ROLLS WITH POTATO AND BASIL CREAM

Servings: 2

INGREDIENTS:

- Aubergine: 1 piece / 340 grams
- Olive oil (virgin): 2 tablespoons / 25 grams
- Potatoes: 4 pieces / 300 grams
- Fresh basil: 15 grams
- Seasoned salt: 3 grams
- White pepper (freshly ground): 1 gram

INSTRUCTIONS:

1. Wash and trim the aubergines and cut lengthwise into 0.5 cm slices. Salt the aubergine slices and leave them to stand for about 20 minutes.

2. Peel the potatoes, wash, dice, and cook in boiling salted water for about 25 minutes or in a steamer for 8 to 10 minutes.

3. Brush the aubergine slices with oil on both sides and grill in the oven or table.

4. Wash and finely chop the basil.

5. Mash the finished potatoes with a fork and mix with herb salt, some oil, pepper, and chopped basil. Add some water or olive oil if the potato mixture is too dry.

6. Shape the potato and basil cream into dumplings, wrap them in the aubergine slices, and secure them with a skewer.

7. Tip: these aubergine rolls can also be eaten cold. They are also great as antipasti, for example, for a party!

NUTRITIONAL VALUES:

- Calories 254
- Protein 5.32g
- Carbohydrates 28.44g
- Fat 12.90g

NETTLE SOUP

Servings: 2

INGREDIENTS:

- Nettle: 180 grams
- Potatoes: 4 pieces / 250 grams
- Onion: 1 piece / 80 grams
- Olive oil: 6 tablespoons / 50 grams
- Vegetable broth (yeast-free, gluten-free, without glutamate): 500 milliliters
- Water: 300 grams
- Nutmeg (grated): 1 gram
- Salt: 1 gram
- Pepper: 1 gram
- Roasted sesame: 2 tablespoons / 20 grams

INSTRUCTIONS:

1. First, skin the onion for the alkaline nettle soup, cut it into small pieces, and sauté in olive oil.

2. Pluck the nettle leaves, wash them, put them in the pot, and steam them until they fall apart.

3. Potato, peel, dice finely, and add. Top up with the vegetable broth and let simmer for about 30 minutes, then puree finely and dilute with water if necessary. Meanwhile, toast the sesame seeds in a pan.

4. Season with salt, pepper, and nutmeg, arrange on a plate, and sprinkle with sesame seeds. The delicious nettle soup is ready!

5. If the nettle soup is needed as a light meal, omit or puree the sesame seeds and onions, depending on the severity.

NUTRITIONAL VALUES:

- Calories 473
- Protein 11.99g
- Carbohydrates 25.19g
- Fat 35.95g

PARSLEY SALAD

Servings: 4

INGREDIENTS:

- Fresh parsley: 120 grams
- Fresh peppermint: 30 grams
- Tomatoes: 4 pieces / 250 grams
- Red onions: 2 pieces / 80 grams
- Garlic cloves: 2 pieces / 4 grams
- Sesame: 8 tablespoons / 40 grams
- Lemon: 1 piece / 35 grams
- Salt: 1 teaspoon / 5 grams
- Pepper: 2 grams
- Ground coriander: 1 gram
- Olive oil (virgin): 5 tablespoons / 40 grams

INSTRUCTIONS:

1. Wash some mint and three whole bunches of parsley, pluck off the stalks, and chop finely.
2. Put the sesame seeds in a coated pan and toast until light brown. Wash, quarter, and core the tomatoes. Cut tomatoes into small cubes. Peel and chop the garlic.
3. Squeeze the lemon and mix the lemon juice with the oil, sesame, salt, coriander, pepper, and garlic.
4. Mix the parsley, tomatoes, and dressing. Let the parsley salad stand for about 10 minutes. Sprinkle with sesame and serve.

NUTRITIONAL VALUES:

- Calories 188
- Protein 4.74g
- Carbohydrates 7.15g
- Fat 15.50g

LENTIL FLOUR BREAD

Servings: 20

INGREDIENTS:

- Lentil flour (red): 175 grams
- Teff flour: 175 grams
- Sesame: 40 grams
- Pumpkin seeds: 80 grams
- Psyllium husks: 4 tablespoons / 16g
- Salt: 1 teaspoon / 5g
- Baking soda: 1 teaspoon / 4g
- Water: 400 grams

INSTRUCTIONS:

1. Put the dry ingredients (lentil flour, teff flour, psyllium husks, sesame, pumpkin seeds, salt, and baking soda) in a bowl and mix well.

2. Add water and knead with a mixer, your hands, or a bread-kneading machine. The batter will remain relatively liquid. Leave to soak for 10 to 15 minutes.

3. Grease the bread tin or line it with baking paper, fill in the lentil flour and teff flour dough, cut lengthwise on the top, and sprinkle with more seeds.

4. Preheat the oven to 170°c. Bake on the middle rack of the oven, testing the doneness after 50 minutes. Stick a wooden skewer into the lentil flour and teff flour bread. If no dough sticks to it, the bread is ready. Otherwise, continue baking for up to 15 minutes.

5. Take the bread out of the mold immediately. Allow cooling on a wire rack for 20 minutes before slicing. The lentil flour and teff flour bread make about 25 slices.

NUTRITIONAL VALUES:

- Calories 315
- Protein 11.03g
- Carbohydrates 8.59g
- Fat 2.57g

OVEN CHILI SQUASH

Servings: 4

INGREDIENTS:

- 1 piece (1400g) Hokkaido pumpkin
- 3 pieces (15g) chili peppers
- 1 tablespoon (20g) honey
- 4 tablespoons (25g) organic lemon juice
- 1/2 teaspoon (1g) ground coriander
- 6 tablespoons (25g) olive oil
- 1 teaspoon (5g) salt
- 1g black pepper

INSTRUCTIONS:

1. Wash the Hokkaido squash and place it whole on a baking sheet in the oven to soften it for slicing. Bake at 150 degrees for 15-25 minutes. Let the pre-cooked Hokkaido cool down, cut it in half, remove the seeds and stalk, and cut it into slices or wedges. The Hokkaido does not (!) Have to be peeled.

2. Clean, deseed and finely chop red chilies. Mix in the olive oil, honey, lemon juice, and coriander.

3. Place Hokkaido pumpkin slices on a clean baking sheet and mix them with the chili marinade. Cook in a preheated oven at 180 degrees for 15-20 minutes. Stir in between if necessary.

4. After baking, season the chili squash with salt and pepper and serve. Enough as a side dish for 4 people. As a main course for 2!

NUTRITIONAL VALUES

- Calories 163
- Protein 4.03g
- Carbohydrates 20.49g
- Fat 6.80g

MILLET PUMPKIN MASH

Servings: 4

INGREDIENTS:

- 400g pumpkin, peeled and diced
- 200g potatoes, peeled and diced
- 150g millet
- 400ml water
- 1 and 1/2 pieces (200g) organic apple, cored and diced
- 100g naturally cloudy apple juice
- 1 tablespoon (15g) virgin rapeseed oil

INSTRUCTIONS:

1. Wash, peel, and dice the pumpkin and potatoes. Cover and simmer with the millet and 400 ml water in a saucepan at the medium level for approx. 15 minutes.

2. Wash, peel, core, and dice the apples and cook for 5 minutes. Stir the millet and pumpkin mash constantly so that nothing burns.

3. Remove from the stove, add apple juice, and puree as finely as you like.

4. Note: once cool, you can freeze the millet-pumpkin mash in portions.

NUTRITIONAL VALUES:

- Calories 271
- Protein 6.23g
- Carbohydrates 48.12g
- Fat 5.38g

ZUCCHINI SPAGHETTI WITH SESAME SALMON AND AVOCADO PESTO

Servings: 2

INGREDIENTS:

- 3 pieces (600g) zucchini, sliced
- 250g organic salmon fillet, skin removed and cut into chunks
- 3 tablespoons (25g) sesame seeds
- 1 piece (150g) avocado, peeled and sliced
- 40g fresh basil leaves, chopped
- 50g sheep cheese, crumbled
- 40g pine nuts
- 1 lemon, juiced (about 50g)
- 4 tablespoons (30g) refined rapeseed oil
- 5g salt

INSTRUCTIONS:

1. For the zucchini spaghetti (zoodles), wash the zucchini and use a spiral cutter to make vegetable noodles.

2. For the avocado pesto, peel and stone the avocado. Rinse the basil and pluck the stalks. Blend the avocado, basil, feta cheese, 2 tablespoons oil, pine nuts, and lemon juice into a cream. Set aside some pine nuts and basil leaves for decoration.

3. Roughly dice the salmon. Spread the sesame seeds on a plate and roll the salmon cubes. Fry on all sides in a pan with 2 tablespoons of oil. After frying, salt and drizzle with lemon juice.

4. At the same time, cook the zucchini spaghetti in simmering salted water for about 3 to 4 minutes and drain. Roast the remaining pine nuts in a pan.

5. Serve zucchini spaghetti with sesame salmon, avocado pesto, and pine nuts.

NUTRITIONAL VALUES:

- Calories 793
- Protein 44.12g
- Carbohydrates 14.17g
- Fat 62.01g

CREAM OF ASPARAGUS

Servings: 4

INGREDIENTS:

- 400g fresh asparagus, woody ends removed and cut into 1-inch pieces
- 1 small potato, peeled and diced
- 1/2 small sweet onion, chopped
- 1/2 leek, white and light green parts only, sliced
- 600ml vegetable broth
- Olive oil
- Salt and pepper

INSTRUCTIONS:

1. Wash the asparagus and cut off the lower end with your fingers. You have to feel the stem and start where it cracks.
2. Remove the tips and reserve them for decorating the plate. Chop the rest of the asparagus.
3. Peel the onion and clean the leek. Finely chop them.
4. Pour a splash of oil into a pot and fry the onion and leek until translucent, about five minutes.
5. Peel the potato and crush it into pieces.
6. Put the potato and asparagus in the casserole.
7. Add the broth and cook everything together, over medium-high heat, for about fifteen minutes, until they are tender.
8. Shred the vegetables. If the cream has become a little thick, you can add a little more broth and, conversely, if it is too liquid, return it to the pot and cook until it thickens.
9. Put a little oil in a pan and grill the tips of the asparagus. Use them to decorate the cream.

NUTRITIONAL VALUES:

- Calories: 115 kcal
- Carbohydrates: 19.8 g
- Protein: 4.2 g
- Fat: 2.6 g
- Fiber: 4.3 g

CUCUMBER SALAD

Servings: 2

INGREDIENTS:

- 1 tomato, diced
- 2 medium cucumbers, diced
- 1 medium carrot, peeled and grated
- 1 small green bell pepper, diced
- 1/2 cup lamb's lettuce
- 1/2 cup chopped fresh cilantro
- 2 tablespoons lemon juice
- 1/4 cup cashews
- Extra virgin olive oil
- Salt and pepper

INSTRUCTIONS:

1. Peel cucumbers and cut them into slices. Could you put them in a salad bowl?
2. Wash the tomato and cut it into not very large pieces.
3. Remove the skin from the carrot, and with a peeler, remove thin strips. Clean and wash the pepper and cut it into julienne strips.
4. Add the tomato, carrot strips, pepper, and lamb's lettuce to the salad bowl. Mix well and season to taste.
5. Combine the chopped cilantro, oil, and lime juice to make the dressing.
6. Pour over the salad and toss.
7. Decorate with cashews.

NUTRITIONAL VALUES:

- Calories: 234
- Fat: 17g
- Carbohydrates: 20g
- Fiber: 4g
- Protein: 5g

PAPAYA SMOOTHIE

Servings: 1

INGREDIENTS:

- 1 papaya, peeled, seeded and chopped
- 1 carrot, peeled and chopped
- 1/2 mango, peeled and chopped
- 1/2 banana, peeled and chopped
- 1 inch piece of ginger, peeled and grated
- 1 tablespoon pumpkin seeds
- 1 heaping tablespoon of yogurt
- 1/2 teaspoon turmeric
- 3/4 cup orange juice
- Ice

INSTRUCTIONS:

1. Put all the ingredients in a blender or shaker except the ice.
2. Beat until a creamy mixture is left.
3. Serve with ice cubes or crushed ice.

NUTRITIONAL VALUES:

- Calories: 321
- Fat: 6.7g
- Carbohydrate: 66.1g
- Fiber: 8.6g
- Protein: 7.5g

STUFFED PINEAPPLE

Servings: 1

INGREDIENTS:

- 1 frozen banana
- 1/4 cup non-dairy milk (such as almond, coconut or soy milk)
- 1/2 small avocado
- 2 handfuls of baby spinach
- 1/2 pineapple (to use as a container)
- 3/4 cup fresh pineapple chunks
- 1 teaspoon flax seeds
- For decoration:
- Pumpkin and sunflower seeds
- Raspberries
- Dehydrated coconut

INSTRUCTIONS:

1. Cut the pineapple in two and carefully empty the inside. Reserve the shell, as it will be the bowl for this dish.

2. Place the peeled frozen banana, milk, diced avocado, washed spines, pineapple chunks (leave a few for garnish), and flaxseeds into a blender or mixer and blend on high speed.

3. Pour the mixture into the pineapple peel when you get a creamy texture.

4. Decorate with raspberries, small pineapple pieces, coconut flakes, and pumpkin seeds.

NUTRITIONAL VALUES:

- Calories: 412
- Fat: 20g
- Carbohydrates: 63g
- Fiber: 15g
- Protein: 6g

ANTI-INFLAMMATORY SALAD

Servings: 4

INGREDIENTS:

- 4 cups baby spinach
- 2 1/2 cups strawberries, sliced
- 1 avocado, sliced
- 1/2 cup chopped basil
- 1/2 cup toasted pistachios
- 1/4 cup olive oil
- 2 tablespoons balsamic vinegar
- 1 clove garlic, minced

INSTRUCTIONS:

1. Wash the spinach and dry it with kitchen paper.
2. Remove the stems and put them in a bowl. If you prefer, chop the leaves.
3. Add the washed and cut strawberries, the sliced avocado, the chopped basil, and the pistachios.
4. Cover with a strawberry dressing. To do so, pass through the blender half a cup of strawberries, the oil, the vinegar, and a whole, peeled garlic clove. Beat until creamy, about a minute.

NUTRITIONAL VALUES:

- Calories: 306 kcal
- Fat: 25g
- Carbohydrates: 19g
- Fiber: 7g
- Protein: 5g

GARLIC AND LEMON SPINACH

Servings: 3

INGREDIENTS:

- 1 tablespoon olive oil
- 3 garlic cloves, cut into thin slices
- A pinch of red pepper flakes
- 2 bunches of spinach, stemmed, washed, and dried
- Juice of a lemon
- Salt and black pepper to taste

INSTRUCTIONS:

1. Warm up the oil in a frying pan on medium heat.
2. Gently cook the garlic and red pepper flakes for approximately 3 minutes until the garlic turns golden.
3. Begin cooking the spinach and use tongs to move any uncooked spinach to the bottom of the pan until it wilts entirely, for about 5 minutes.
4. Remove any excess water from the bottom of the pan.
5. Mix in the lemon juice and add salt and black pepper to taste.

NUTRITIONAL VALUES:

- Calories: 81
- Fat: 6.5g
- Carbohydrates: 5.3g
- Fiber: 2.7g
- Protein: 3.6g

GINGER SALMON

Servings: 2

INGREDIENTS:

- 1 tablespoon coconut oil
- 1/4 cup water
- 2 teaspoons grated fresh ginger
- 1 tablespoon umeboshi plum vinegar
- 2 4-ounce wild salmon fillets
- Lime slices to decorate

INSTRUCTIONS:

1. Prepare the marinade by combining oil, water, ginger, and vinegar. Place the fish in a shallow baking dish, cover with the marinade, and refrigerate for at least 30 minutes.
2. Preheat oven to a low broil setting.
3. Remove the fish from the marinade and reserve the rest as a spread.
4. In an ovenproof dish, grill fish skin side down for 6-8 minutes, basting twice with the remaining marinade.
5. Garnish with lime wedges and serve.

NUTRITIONAL VALUES:

- Calories: 200
- Fat: 10g
- Carbohydrate: 3g
- Fiber: 0g
- Protein: 24g

PUMPKIN AND CAULIFLOWER CURRY

Servings: 4

INGREDIENTS:

- 1 tbsp vegetable oil, ghee, or grapeseed oil
- 1 cup chopped yellow onion
- 3 garlic cloves, minced
- 4 tablespoons curry paste
- 3 cups pumpkin, cut into 1/2-inch cubes
- 3 cups cauliflower florets
- 15.5 ounces chickpeas, drained (1 can)
- 13.5 ounces of coconut milk (1 can)
- 1 1/2 cups of water, plus more as needed
- 1 teaspoon kosher salt
- 1/4 teaspoon black pepper
- 4 ounces baby spinach, about 4 cups
- 1 cup frozen peas
- 1/2 cup coriander leaves
- 4 cups of cooked basmati rice
- Naan bread, optional

INSTRUCTIONS:

1. Warm up one tablespoon of oil on medium heat in a large and deep frying pan.
2. Sauté the onions and garlic over medium-low heat for 10 minutes until they are tender and have turned a light color.
3. Once the onions are soft, mix in the curry paste and stir for one minute.

4. Add the pumpkin, cauliflower, chickpeas, coconut milk, water, salt, and pepper. Bring to a boil, then reduce heat to low and let it simmer (covered) for around 35 minutes, occasionally stirring, until the squash and cauliflower have become tender.

5. Sample the sauce and add more seasoning if required. Add water to get the desired consistency if the sauce is too thick.

6. Mix in spinach, peas, and cilantro leaves. Cook over low heat until the spinach has gently wilted.

7. Serve with basmati rice and naan bread if desired.

NUTRITIONAL VALUES:

- Calories: 537 kcal
- Fat: 17 g
- Carbohydrates: 85 g
- Fiber: 13 g
- Protein: 16 g

FIRE-ROASTED PUMPKIN AND BRUSSELS

Servings: 4

INGREDIENTS:

- 1/2 large pumpkin, peeled and cut into 1-inch cubes
- 1 pound brussels sprouts, trimmed and halved
- 2 tablespoons avocado oil, split
- 2 teaspoons salt, divided
- 1 teaspoon cinnamon, divided
- 2 tablespoons maple syrup
- 1/2 cup nuts (pecans, walnuts, etc.)
- 1/2 cup dried fruit (cranberries, raisins, etc.)

INSTRUCTIONS:

1. Preheat oven to 204 degrees Celsius.
2. Peel and seed squash, then cut into 1" cubes. Drizzle with avocado oil, salt, and cinnamon on a parchment-lined baking sheet. Toss to coat evenly.
3. Wash the brussels sprouts, trim the ends, and cut them in half. Drizzle with avocado oil, salt, and cinnamon on a parchment-lined baking sheet. Toss to coat evenly and place face down.
4. Bake the squash and brussels sprouts for 20-25 minutes or until the bottom sides start to crisp. Flip it over and bake for another 10 minutes.
5. Once cooled, combine the brussels sprouts, pumpkin, dried fruit, and walnuts in a large bowl. Drizzle with maple syrup, season with more salt and cinnamon if desired, and mix to combine.

NUTRITIONAL VALUES:

- Calories: 174 kcal
- Protein: 4 g
- Fat: 11 g
- Carbohydrates: 20 g
- Fiber: 5 g

ROAST TURKEY

Servings: 2

INGREDIENTS:

- 1 whole young turkey, thawed
- 6 garlic cloves
- 1 whole onion, cut into quarters
- 2 celery stalks, cut into large chunks
- 1 whole orange, cut into quarters
- 3 sprigs of thyme
- 2 sprigs of rosemary
- Salt and pepper
- 3 tablespoons olive oil
- 3 tablespoons butter
- 1/2 cup white wine

INSTRUCTIONS:

To roast the turkey:

1. Make sure the turkey is completely thawed. Let the turkey come to close to room temperature, about an hour and a half depending on the size.

2. Discard the turkey packaging and remove the giblets from the cavity. Dry turkey all over, so the skin is crisp.

3. On a sturdy cutting board, place the turkey breast side down. Locating the spine, cut along one side of it with the designated kitchen shears. This will take more effort than you think - you're cutting gristle and bone!

4. With the backbone removed, turn the turkey over on the cutting board so that the cut side is on the board and the

breast side is up. Press down on the breasts with both hands until the backbone snaps and the turkey is flat.

5. Transfer the turkey to a baking sheet.

To season and cook:

1. Preheat oven to 230 degrees Celsius.

2. Melt the butter in a small skillet, then combine it with salt, pepper, and olive oil. Once combined, spread the mixture all over the turkey, on both sides.

3. Arrange the garlic, onion, celery, orange, thyme, and rosemary around the turkey, and pour the white wine into the bottom of the baking tray. This will also help with seasoning any sauce you make afterward.

4. Place the turkey in the oven for 20 minutes, then turn the temperature to 176°cfor at least an hour. Cook until skin is golden brown and the thickest part of the breast reads74°c.

5. Remove from oven and let rest 30 minutes before cutting and serving.

NUTRITIONAL VALUES:

- Calories: 153 kcal
- Protein: 28 g
- Fat: 4 g
- Carbohydrates: 0 g
- Fiber: 0 g

DINNER RECIPES

WARM SALAD WITH PINE NUTS, TOMATO, AND BASIL

Serving: 4

INGREDIENTS:

- 400g mix of tender sprouts (such as broccoli, alfalfa, radish, etc.)
- 8 pear tomatoes, halved
- 1 clove garlic, minced
- 4 sprigs of basil, leaves chopped
- 2 tablespoons balsamic vinegar
- 1 red onion, sliced
- 20g peeled pine nuts
- Extra virgin olive oil
- Pepper
- Salt

INSTRUCTIONS:

1. Preheat the oven to 140°c. Wash and dry the basil; peel the garlic. Crush the basil and garlic together with 1 dl of oil. 2.

2. Wash the tomatoes, dry them, and cut them in half lengthwise. Arrange them on the baking sheet, brush them with the basil oil, splash them, and sprinkle them with a few drops of vinegar. Add the pine nuts and bake them for about 1 hour.

3. Peel the onion and cut it into feathers. Clean the salad sprouts, wash them, and drain them.

4. Dress them with the remaining vinegar, oil, and salt, and stir, so they are impregnated on all sides. Add the pine nuts and onion, and mix well.

5. Place 4 pastry rings on as many plates as possible and fill them with the previous mixture.

6. Arrange the tomatoes on top, carefully remove the rings and serve the salad immediately.

NUTRITIONAL VALUES:

- Calories: 168 kcal
- Fat: 13.3 g
- Carbohydrates: 11.6 g
- Fiber: 2.8 g
- Protein: 3.1 g

SAUTÉED MUSHROOM AND ZUCCHINI SPAGHETTI WITH SCRAMBLED TOFU AND CASHEW NUTS

Serving: 4

INGREDIENTS:

- 400g shiitake mushrooms (or other mushrooms), sliced
- 2 zucchini, sliced
- 1 red onion, sliced
- 1 clove garlic, minced
- A handful of cashews
- 6-7 chive stalks, chopped
- 4 tablespoons of olive oil
- Pepper and salt

For the tofu scramble:

- 250g firm tofu, crumbled
- 1 tablespoon tamari
- 1/2 teaspoon smoked paprika
- 1 tablespoon nutritional yeast
- 1 tablespoon turmeric
- 2 tablespoons of olive oil
- Sea salt or kala namak salt

INSTRUCTIONS:

1. Take the tofu out of the package and wrap it in a cloth or kitchen paper, put a weight (for example, a cutting board) on top, and let it dry well.

2. Meanwhile, wash the zucchini, remove them, and cut them into spirals with a spiralizer or thin, long strips with the help of a mandolin or peeler.

3. Blanch the zucchini spirals in boiling salted water for 2 minutes. Drain and quickly immerse them in a bowl with very cold water. Drain again and reserve.

4. Peel the onion, cut it into strips, and fry them in a wide frying pan with 2 tablespoons of olive oil for about 8-10 minutes over low heat. Add the zucchini spirals, salt, pepper, and sauté for a few moments. Add half of the chopped chives.

NUTRITIONAL VALUES:

- Calories: 374 kcal
- Carbohydrates: 14 g
- Protein: 14 g
- Fat: 30 g
- Fiber: 5 g

FENNEL AND ZUCCHINI CREAM WITH VEGETABLE CHIPS

Serving: 4

INGREDIENTS:

For the soup:

- 2 large zucchini, chopped
- 1 fennel bulb, chopped
- 1 leek, chopped
- 1 potato, chopped
- 1 liter of water or vegetable broth
- Extra virgin olive oil
- Nutmeg, pepper, and salt

For the chips:

- 2 carrots, thinly sliced
- 1 beetroot, thinly sliced
- 1/2 cassava, thinly sliced
- 1/2 zucchini, thinly sliced
- Mild olive oil
- Aromatic herbs or spices (such as paprika, garlic powder, or cumin)
- Fresh rosemary or fennel leaves to decorate

INSTRUCTIONS:

1. If you make the chips at home, you must prepare them beforehand. You only need to cut the vegetables into very thin slices (2-3 mm), preferably with a mandolin or a vegetable peeler, put them in a large bowl, and add olive oil and the spices or aromatic herbs with which you want to season them (for example, curry, dill, paprika, garlic

powder, turmeric, cumin, rosemary, thyme. Mix them well so that they are impregnated. Then you dehydrate them in the dehydrator or, if you don't have one, in the oven itself: you put it at a temperature of 100-150oc and bake it for between 30 and 90 minutes, depending on the vegetable. You will have to open the oven occasionally to let the steam out or leave the door ajar and place a wooden spoon across it to prevent it from closing.

2. When preparing the cream, wash the zucchini and cut them into pieces. If you want, you can also peel them. Clean the fennel, removing the hardest base and cutting it into strips. Peel the potato.

3. Heat a little oil in a large saucepan and fry the leek over low heat until transparent. Stir often with a wooden spoon, so it doesn't burn.

4. Add the courgettes, the fennel, and the potato, let it poach slightly with the lid for a couple of minutes, and cover with the water or vegetable broth. Season to taste and cook for about 20 minutes, until the vegetables are tender and the potato is done.

5. Remove the leek, fennel, zucchini, and potato preparation from the heat, grind it, and season with salt and pepper. Add nutmeg, spread the vegetable chips on top, and decorate with rosemary or fennel leaves.

NUTRITIONAL VALUES:

- Calories: 192
- Fat: 10g
- Carbohydrates: 23g
- Fiber: 7g
- Protein: 6g

BUCKWHEAT TIMBALE, PEAS, AND TOMATO WITH SPROUTS

Serving: 4

INGREDIENTS:

- 400g buckwheat
- 800ml of water
- 2 large carrots, diced
- 1 large, very ripe tomato, diced
- 200g peas
- 15g radish sprouts
- Turmeric
- Oregano
- Pepper
- Extra virgin olive oil
- Salt

INSTRUCTIONS:

1. Cook the buckwheat and let it cool.
2. Peel a carrot and cut it into small dice. Put a pan on the fire with a little olive oil and cook the carrot with the pan covered. After about 15 minutes, or when it is tender, remove and reserve. Repeat the process with the chopped tomato.
3. Cook the peas in salted water for 7 minutes. Reserve 100 g of peas to decorate, sautéed in a pan with a little olive oil, and seasoned.
4. Divide the buckwheat into three equal parts. Crush one part with the tomato, another with the carrot, and the last with 100 g peas. Add to all a jet of oil and salt and pepper.

5. Season as follows: carrot puree with turmeric, tomato with paprika, and peas with oregano. Integrate the spices well and reserve.

6. With the help of a stainless steel ring, on a plate, arrange the first layer of the pea mixture, the second of the carrot, and the third of the tomato. Remove the hoop. Decorate with the reserved sautéed peas and sprouts.

NUTRITIONAL VALUES:

- Calories: 444 kcal
- Carbohydrates: 77 g
- Protein: 17 g
- Fat: 8 g
- Fiber: 13 g

AVOCADO, ZUCCHINI, AND CHICKPEA HUMMUS SERVED WITH CRUDITÉS

Serving: 6-8

INGREDIENTS:

- 2 courgettes, chopped
- 8-9 tablespoons tahini (preferably raw sesame)
- 1-2 avocados
- 250g chickpeas
- 2 tablespoons nutritional yeast
- 1 lemon, juiced
- 2 garlic cloves
- Sea salt (to taste)
- Water and olive oil, if necessary

INSTRUCTIONS:

1. Mix all the ingredients in a blender until you get a homogeneous texture. If it is too thick, add water and olive oil until you get the desired texture.

2. Serve this hummus with sticks or little sticks, which you can prepare with celery, carrot, cucumber, or red pepper. Endives are also very good.

NUTRITIONAL VALUES:

Calories: 230

Fat: 16g

Carbohydrates: 16g

Fiber: 7g

Protein: 8g

SALMON PAPILLOTE WITH LEEKS

Serving: 4

INGREDIENTS:

- 4 salmon loins or ingots, cleaned
- 1 leek, chopped
- 2 carrots, peeled and chopped
- 2cm piece of fresh ginger, peeled and grated
- 60ml teriyaki sauce
- 60ml port wine
- 4 star anise
- 15ml sesame or sunflower oil
- Ground black pepper

INSTRUCTIONS:

1. We will start by preheating the oven to 180°c. Chop the carrots in Juliana, as well as the leeks and ginger. Then we put a pan on the fire with the oil and sauté the vegetables until tender.

2. Divide the vegetables into four equal parts, and prepare four sheets of baking paper or aluminum foil about 30 by 40 centimeters. We put a little of the vegetables, place the salmon with salt and pepper and cover it with the rest.

3. We put a spoonful of teriyaki sauce in each package, the port, and an aniseed star. We close the papillote and bake for 10 minutes.

NUTRITIONAL VALUES:

- Calories: 374 kcal
- Total fat: 14g
- Carbohydrates: 21g
- Fiber: 3g
- Protein: 38g

EGGPLANT, TOMATO, AND SPINACH CURRY

Serving: 4

INGREDIENTS:

- 1 onion, chopped
- 2 garlic cloves, minced
- 50g fresh ginger, peeled and grated
- 1 cayenne chili, chopped
- 10g ground cumin
- 10g garam masala (ground cumin, cinnamon, and cloves)
- 10g ground coriander
- 5g ground turmeric
- 75g concentrated tomato
- 50g sunflower oil
- 2 eggplants, chopped
- 2 tomatoes, chopped
- 80g fresh spinach
- 300ml vegetable soup
- Extra virgin olive oil
- Salt

INSTRUCTIONS:

1. In a food processor, grind the onion, peeled and chopped; the garlic cloves, peeled; the fresh ginger, also peeled; the cayenne pepper, without the seeds (which is what itches), the cumin, garam masala, coriander, turmeric, concentrated tomato, and sunflower oil. We stop and reserve when we have homogeneous pasta without remains or stumbling blocks of any ingredient.

2. Wash the eggplant and tomatoes. Cut the first one into cubes of approximately 2 cm and the tomatoes into eight wedges each. Wash the spinach and reserve. Heat a couple of tablespoons of olive oil in a wide casserole and add the pasta that we have reserved. Add the eggplant cubes, stir, and cook for 10 minutes over low heat.

3. Add the vegetable broth and cook gently for 30 minutes. Add the tomatoes and cook for 10 more minutes. Finally, add the spinach and cook again for a few minutes until they have softened. Season to taste and serve immediately with fresh cilantro sprinkled on the surface.

NUTRITIONAL VALUES:

- Calories: 218 kcal
- Carbohydrates: 18 g
- Protein: 5 g
- Fat: 15 g
- Fiber: 7 g

SALAD WITH GRILLED GOAT CHEESE

Serving: 2

INGREDIENTS:

- 150g assorted buds (such as arugula, spinach, and lettuce)
- 20g pine nuts
- 20g sliced goat cheese
- 12 red grapes
- Apple vinegar
- Extra virgin olive oil

INSTRUCTIONS:

1. Wash and drain the sprouts and sage well, so the salad does not burn. Wash, dry, and slice the grapes. We distribute in a serving tray, or individual bowls, the varied sprouts and the red sage as a base, and on top, we distribute the grapes and pine nuts.

2. Separately, we heat a skillet over high heat and make the goat roll in slices of about 4 cm, more or less, on each side. We can also use a kitchen torch, which will take less time. We spread the goat cheese over the salad and season it to our liking. This salad is a bit sweet, so I recommend a rather acidic dressing to contrast the flavors.

NUTRITIONAL VALUES:

- Calories: 355 per serving
- Fat: 26g
- Carbohydrates: 16g
- Fiber: 3g
- Protein: 15g

ROASTED CAULIFLOWER WITH SPICES

Serving: 4

INGREDIENTS:

- 1 large cauliflower
- 80-100g raw flaked almonds
- 1 tsp fennel seeds
- 1 tsp cumin seeds
- 1 tsp coriander seeds
- 1/2 tsp mustard seeds
- 1/2 tsp black peppercorns
- 2 cloves
- 1 tbsp ground turmeric
- 1 pinch of cayenne or hot paprika
- Fresh parsley or coriander
- 1 thick plain yogurt
- 1/2 tsp granulated garlic
- 1/2 lemon
- Salt
- Extra virgin olive oil

INSTRUCTIONS:

1. Preheat the oven to 160°c and prepare a tray or dish. Extend the almonds and separate the spices into grains or seeds. Cut the cauliflower into florets and wash very well, draining the water. Toast the almonds and the spices for about 5 minutes, carefully watching them not burn. Remove and raise the temperature to 220°c.

2. Crush the toasted spices in a mortar or grind with a grinder or chopper. Add the ground turmeric and cayenne or hot paprika until you have a more or less homogeneous mixture. Place the cauliflower on a large plate or bowl and mix it with the spices, a drizzle of olive oil, and a pinch of salt.

3. Spread on a baking tray and roast, occasionally stirring, for about 20-25 minutes. It should be al dente, tender on the inside but slightly hard, toasted on the outside. Adjust the baking time to your taste.

4. Drain the liquid from the yogurt, season with salt and pepper, add the lemon zest and juice, and a little olive oil. Beat well until you have a creamy texture. Wash and chop the parsley or cilantro, serve with the cauliflower, and add the reserved almonds.

NUTRITIONAL VALUES:

- Calories: 265
- Fat: 19g
- Carbohydrates: 18g
- Fiber: 9g
- Protein: 11g

TUNA IN MANGO CURRY SAUCE

Serving: 2

INGREDIENTS:

- 1/2 sweet onion or 1 spring onion, finely chopped
- 1/2 garlic clove, minced
- 1 teaspoon curry mix
- 1 pinch cayenne
- 1/2 teaspoon ground turmeric
- 2 tuna steaks
- White wine
- 1 lemon
- 1 medium ripe and aromatic mango (approximately 200 ml of pulp), diced
- 1 tablespoon grated coconut
- Black pepper
- Salt
- Parsley or cilantro
- Extra virgin olive oil

INSTRUCTIONS:

1. Cut the mango in half and extract the pulp with a large spoon, removing the bone. You have to try to make the most of all the juices. Chop and grind in a food processor or blender with a pinch of salt and the juice of half a lemon. Book.

2. Dry the tuna loins with kitchen paper and cut them into cubes of more or less the same size. Chop the onion and the garlic clove. Heat a little olive oil in a pan or casserole and

add ingredients and spices. Brown until the onion is transparent over low heat, and add a pinch of salt. Add the tuna, season, and water with the wine. Cook for a few minutes over high heat until the fish is browned on both sides.

3. Add the mango to the pan, lower the heat, and stir well. Add the rest of the lemon juice to the grated coconut. Taste the sauce and season more if necessary. Cook until it reduces as desired, adding a little more wine or water if it dries up too much. Serve with finely chopped parsley or cilantro.

NUTRITIONAL VALUES:

- Calories: 357
- Protein: 44g
- Fat: 11g
- Carbohydrates: 18g Fiber: 3g

BROCCOLI COUSCOUS WITH TURMERIC EGG

Serving: 1

INGREDIENTS:

- 1 small broccoli
- Fresh ginger, grated, to taste
- 1 small garlic clove, minced
- 5ml sherry vinegar
- 5ml lemon juice
- Lemon zest, to taste
- 1 teaspoon caraway seeds
- 1 teaspoon cumin seeds
- Dried thyme, to taste
- 1 egg
- 2 tablespoons ground turmeric
- Ground black pepper
- Salt
- Extra virgin olive oil

INSTRUCTIONS:

1. Cut broccoli florets and leaves. Please, do not throw away the trunk; it can be used in creams and soups or even steamed or roasted in the oven with other vegetables. A delicious tender interior is discovered if the base's woodiest part is cut.

2. Gently wash the florets and leaves, drain, and chop with a food processor or chopper. It can also be grated or roughly chopped with a good knife -and be very careful-. You have to get a very fine grainy texture, like real couscous.

3. Heat a nonstick skillet and lightly toast the cumin and caraway seeds. Add a little oil with the grated ginger and the minced garlic clove. Stir a few times until they brown, over medium heat, and add the broccoli with the thyme. Also, add the large chopped broccoli leaves, reserving the small ones (optional).

4. Sauté for a minute, add the vinegar and lemon juice, and stir well. Add salt and pepper and sauté over high heat for a few more minutes. You can leave the texture you want but don't need much cooking time. Keep warm while we cook the egg.

5. Heat a saucepan with plenty of water and one or two heaping teaspoons of turmeric, stirring well so that it dissolves. Bring to a boil without letting it boil, and cook the egg by poaching it as usual. The silicone utensils on the market are going well and are not too complicated. Take out after 4-8 minutes, depending on how we like it curdled.

6. Serve the false broccoli couscous adjusting the salt level. Top with the freshly made egg and add a pinch of salt flakes and freshly ground black pepper. Accompany the broccoli leaves that we have reserved, if applicable.

NUTRITIONAL VALUES:
- Calories: 302 kcal
- Fat: 21 g
- Carbohydrates: 19 g
- Fiber: 7 g
- Protein: 15 g

SALMON ITALIAN WITH POTATOES AND VEGETABLES

Serving: 2

INGREDIENTS:

- 200g frozen salmon fillet
- 350g potatoes, peeled and diced
- 1 zucchini (220g), sliced
- 1 red sweet pepper (155g), diced
- 25g pine nuts
- 4 sprigs of fresh rosemary (4g)
- 4g of fresh thyme
- 4 tablespoons (32g) of refined rapeseed oil
- 4 garlic cloves (12g), minced
- 1 lemon (50g), juiced and zested
- 1 teaspoon (5g) of salt
- 1g of pepper

INSTRUCTIONS:

1. Defrost the salmon fillets in good time. Wash and peel the potatoes and boil them in salted water for about 20 minutes. Then drain and cut into slices.

2. Meanwhile, wash and pat dry the thyme and rosemary, and pluck the rosemary needles from the stems. Halve the lemon, cut the flesh into fine pieces without the peel, and roast them with the pine nuts without oil.

3. Peel the garlic and cut it into fine slices. Wash zucchini and peppers and cut them into bite-sized pieces.

4. Heat 2 tablespoons of rapeseed oil in a coated pan, and fry the courgettes, peppers, and potatoes. Shortly before the end of the roasting time, season with thyme, rosemary, garlic, salt, and pepper, then keep warm.

5. Season the salmon fillets on both sides with salt and pepper. Heat 2 tbsp rapeseed oil in a coated pan. Add salmon fillets and fry over medium heat for 5 to 6 minutes.

6. Arrange the salmon on the vegetables and garnish with lemon pine nuts. Cut the second half of the lemon into pieces and place them on the plate.

NUTRITIONAL VALUES:

- Calories 594
- Protein 30.17g
- Carbohydrates 38.74g
- Fat 34.51g

PURSLANE SALAD WITH CUCUMBER AND PEAS

Serving: 4

INGREDIENTS:

- 250g purslane
- 1 cucumber (550g), sliced
- 150g fresh peas
- 4 tablespoons (32g) native linseed oil
- 2 tablespoons (28g) balsamic vinegar
- 1 teaspoon (10g) medium hot mustard
- 1 teaspoon (8g) honey
- 1½ teaspoons (7½ g) salt
- ½ teaspoon (3½ g) pepper
- 200 milligrams (0.2 g) water

INSTRUCTIONS:

1. Bring the water to a boil with a teaspoon of salt. Cook the peas until tender but still has some bite, about five minutes. Drain the peas and let them cool. Rinse the purslane leaves with cold water and drain. Wash the cucumber, quarter lengthwise, and cut it into slices. Place the vegetables in a large salad bowl.

2. Dissolve the remaining half teaspoon of salt in the balsamic vinegar, and stir in the mustard, pepper, and honey. Mix with the linseed oil to make a vinaigrette. Mix the purslane salad with the sauce and serve immediately.

NUTRITIONAL VALUES:

- Calories 217
- Protein 10.59g
- Carbohydrates 22.12g
- Fat 9.16g

TABBOULEH

Serving: 4

INGREDIENTS:

- 150g bulgur
- 4 spring onions, thinly sliced
- 2 beefsteak tomatoes (400g), diced
- 1/2 cucumber (275g), diced
- 50g fresh parsley, chopped
- 50g fresh peppermint, chopped
- 5 tablespoons (30g) lemon juice
- 3 tablespoons (24g) olive oil
- 1 teaspoon (5g) salt
- 1/2 teaspoon (2g) black pepper
- 1/4 teaspoon (1g) paprika
- 300 milliliters water

INSTRUCTIONS:

1. Bring the water to a boil and pour over the bulgur wheat. Cover and leave to swell for 20 minutes.

2. Wash and clean the vegetables and herbs. Remove the stalks of the tomatoes and dice. Cut spring onions into rings. Peel the cucumber. Remove seeds and dice. Finely chop the parsley and mint.

3. Put the vegetables in a bowl. Drain the finished bulgur. Mix the bulgur with the vegetables. Dissolve salt in lemon juice. Stir in pepper and paprika. Mix the lemon juice with the olive oil and dress the tabbouleh with the dressing. Season with salt, pepper, and lemon juice. Leave the tabbouleh to stand for an hour before serving.

NUTRITIONAL VALUES:

- Calories 231
- Protein 7.06g
- Carbohydrates 33.45g
- Fat 7.23g

QUINOA SALAD, THAI STYLE

Serving: 4

INGREDIENTS:

- 200g quinoa
- 400ml water
- 1 red sweet pepper (155g), diced
- 1 carrot (75g), grated
- 1/2 cucumber (275g), diced
- 2 spring onions (60g), thinly sliced
- 30g fresh coriander, chopped
- 2 limes (210g), juiced
- 3 tablespoons (30g) fish sauce
- 5 tablespoons (40g) olive oil
- 1 tablespoon (15g) sugar
- 2 chili peppers (20g), thinly sliced
- 1 pinch (1g) salt

INSTRUCTIONS:

1. Rinse the quinoa well in a colander and drain. In a pot, sauté the quinoa in a tablespoon of olive oil, add 400 ml of water, and bring to a boil with a good pinch of salt. Once bubbling, simmer over low heat until the quinoa has absorbed the water. Let cool and fluff with a fork.

2. Halve the limes and squeeze out the juice. Make the salad dressing from the fish sauce, lime juice, sugar, salt, olive oil, and finely chopped chili peppers. Shaking the ingredients in a tightly fitting jar is quick and easy. The amount of chili peppers depends on your taste. If you like it

spicy, don't remove the seeds. If uncomfortable with the spiciness, use a seedless pod or leave out the chilies altogether.

3. Dice the bell pepper, carrot, and peeled cucumber. Finely chop the spring onions. Roughly chop the coriander leaves and mix them with the salad dressing under the quinoa salad.

NUTRITIONAL VALUES:

- Calories 355
- Protein 8.25g
- Carbohydrates 44.40g
- Fat 14.83g

Printed in April 2023
by Rotomail Italia S.p.A., Vignate (MI) - Italy